CBT INNER CHILD WORKBOOK

HEAL PAST TRAUMA, RESTORE EMOTIONAL
RESILIENCE, AND RECLAIM YOUR JOY WITH
COGNITIVE BEHAVIORAL THERAPY EXERCISES,
JOURNAL PROMPTS, AND SELF-LOVE PRACTICES

LEIGH W. HART

CONTENTS

Introduction   11

1. UNDERSTANDING YOUR INNER CHILD   17
   Introduction to the Concept of the Inner Child   19
   The Ego and the Inner Child   24
   Reparenting Your Wounded Inner Child   26
   Exercise: Assessing Your Current State   28
   Exercise: Getting to Know Your Inner Child   31
   Inner Child Journal Prompts   35

2. FOUNDATIONS OF COGNITIVE BEHAVIORAL
   THERAPY   39
   Basic and Advanced Principles of CBT   41
   The History of CBT   42
   Basic Principles of CBT   44
   CBT and the Inner Child   55
   Exercise: Exploring Your Inner Child's Needs   58
   Exercise: Reframing Unhelpful Thought Patterns   60
   Inner Child Journal Prompts   62

3. UNCOVERING CHILDHOOD AND
   GENERATIONAL TRAUMAS   67
   Identifying Sources of Trauma   68
   Myths About Trauma   75
   Generational Patterns and Beliefs   78
   Inner Child Journal Prompts   91

4. CHALLENGING NEGATIVE BELIEFS AND
   BEHAVIORS   95
   Recognizing and Addressing Negative Thought
   Patterns   96
   Behavior Modification Strategies   102
   Case Studies   105
   Inner Child Journal Prompts   115

5. BUILDING POSITIVE COPING MECHANISMS   121
   Developing Healthy Coping Skills   122
   Mindfulness and Relaxation Techniques   124
   How to Incorporate Mindfulness Into Daily Life   128
   Establishing a Self-Care Routine   130
   Exercise: 30-Day Self-Care Calendar   138
   Inner Child Journal Prompts   140

6. RECONNECTING WITH YOUR INNER CHILD   145
   Healing and Nurturing Your Inner Child   146
   Creative Expression   154
   Forgiveness and Acceptance   156
   Exercise: 30-Day Nurturing and Writing for Your
   Inner Child   162
   Inner Child Journal Prompts   172

7. MOVING FORWARD AND MAINTAINING
   PROGRESS   177
   Setting Goals for the Future   178
   Planning for Long-Term Success   184
   Inner Child Journal Prompts   192

   Conclusion   199
   References   207

The **CBT Inner Child Workbook** is a heartfelt follow-up and companion to my #1 Best Seller, **Reparenting Your Wounded Inner Child.**

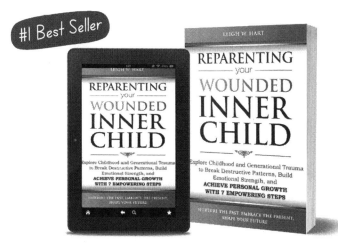

I invite you to deepen your inner child healing journey by discovering the powerful techniques shared in **Reparenting Your Wounded Inner Child.** These resources work together to guide you towards greater self-compassion and emotional healing, providing transformative tools to care for and nurture your inner child.

Leigh W Hart

Amazon.com/Author/LeighWHart

Elevate Your Journey With...

Bonus #1

THREE COMPLIMENTARY SUPPORT WORKBOOKS!

Customized Worksheets:

I have created a customized collection of
95+ journal pages and interactive worksheets that
have been designed to complement the steps,
journal prompts, and exercises discussed in this
book perfectly.

Go to:
CBTInnerChild.LeighWHart.com
to receive your BONUS
printable support materials.

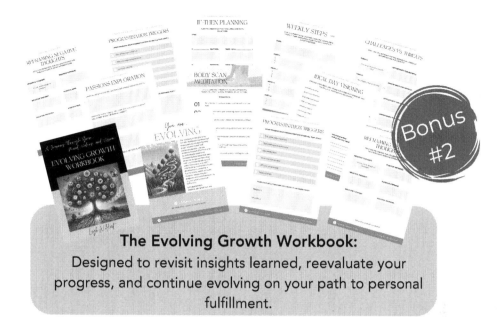

The Evolving Growth Workbook:
Designed to revisit insights learned, reevaluate your progress, and continue evolving on your path to personal fulfillment.

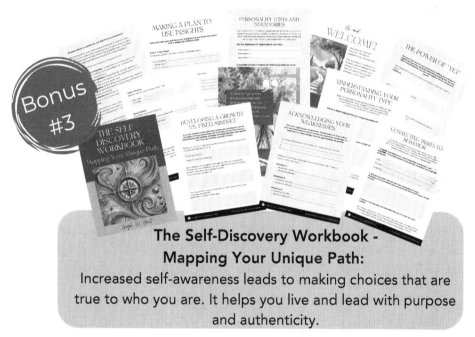

**The Self-Discovery Workbook -
Mapping Your Unique Path:**
Increased self-awareness leads to making choices that are true to who you are. It helps you live and lead with purpose and authenticity.

Go to:
CBTInnerChild.LeighWHart.com
to receive your BONUS
printable support materials.

TRIGGER WARNING:

This book contains discussions regarding childhood traumas, abuse, toxic relationships, and other potentially emotionally triggering material. Please proceed with caution and stop reading if you feel overwhelmed. If you're in need of someone to speak to, you can reach the National Domestic Violence Hotline at 800-799- 7233, or you can contact the Suicide and Crisis Lifeline at 988.

MEDICAL DISCLAIMER:

INTRODUCTION

Meet Christine. She vividly recalls moments amidst the bustling holiday season. The world around her was adorned with the vibrant hues of joy and festivity: twinkling lights, cheerful melodies, and heartwarming holiday movies playing on screens everywhere. But for her, an unsettling feeling lingered. The holidays, traditionally a time of joy and celebration, stirred a deep sense of dread and fear within her. She didn't envision being snuggled around a fire with family and laughter. She didn't have warm, happy memories from her past. Instead, her stomach would churn at the thought of family gatherings because some of those in attendance were responsible for hurting her as a child.

Perhaps you've walked a similar path. You see, even the most spirited people sometimes admit that family parties can be a huge source of stress. We all aim to craft perfect celebrations, choose the most thoughtful gifts, and embrace the spirit of gratitude. Yet, if you've already been navigating the complex path of surviving childhood abuse, the additional pressures can transform into an emotional minefield, unearthing feelings and insecurities you believed were long buried.

For Christine, this meant being bombarded with questions. "Why do you look so sad? Turn that frown upside down! Do you not like the holidays?" Friends and family would question why she couldn't simply join in the holiday fun, unaware of the internal battle she was waging. They would tease her, "Oh look, the 'Grinch' has arrived," believing this was all in good fun. Nevertheless, their words only intensified the pressure, leaving her with a sense of isolation and misunderstanding.

For countless survivors of childhood abuse, family gatherings are not moments of joy but triggers for anxiety and depression. The mere thought of them can force you into distressing situations with those who inflicted pain upon you or those who refused to acknowledge your suffering.

The sights, sounds, and scents can serve as poignant triggers, reviving emotions you've struggled to bury. It becomes a relentless mental tug-of-war. Should you expose yourself to the torment of reliving traumatic memories, or should you decide to shield yourself from the agony, even if it means staying away from loved ones? These were the questions Christine, and many like her, would have to juggle time and time again. Dealing with childhood trauma is complex and often misunderstood.

If you're reading this, you've likely encountered your own share of childhood trauma, unexplained emotional reactions, moments of turbulence in your personal relationships, and difficulties regulating your emotions. You're not alone. In fact, a staggering 60% of adults report experiencing abuse or challenging family circumstances during their childhood (Bakr, n.d.). The wounds from our past can linger, affecting our present, but there is hope for healing and transformation.

This workbook is your companion on the journey to heal your inner child, understand the roots of your emotional struggles, and empower yourself with practical tools for change. It builds upon the foundation laid out in my previous book, *Reparenting Your Wounded Inner Child*, and delves even deeper into the transformative power of Cognitive Behavioral Therapy (CBT).

By the time you finish this workbook, you will not only have a deeper understanding of your past but also a clear plan for building healthier relationships with yourself and others. You'll uncover improved emotional control and a stronger sense of self, giving you the strength to handle life's obstacles. We'll delve into CBT therapy and its role in helping you develop skills and strategies for achieving and maintaining wellness. We'll also explore how it focuses on addressing day-to-day challenges and understanding how perceptions influence emotions.

I am not just an author but a therapist who has witnessed first-hand the transformative impact of these techniques in my private practice. I've watched people like you confront their darkest shadows, emerge stronger, and rewrite their life stories.

I know the struggles because I've been there, too, facing the uphill battle of self-discovery and healing without the guidance we are about to embark upon together.

So, if you're wondering if this is the right book for you if you're seeking the path to personal understanding and emotional well-being, if you long for the day when life no longer feels like a battleground—then rest assured, you are in the right place.

Before we dive into the first chapter, let's set the stage for transformation with these ten affirmations:

1. I consciously foster an environment of serenity and security within myself.
2. I refrain from holding myself responsible for my childhood experiences or past traumas.
3. Establishing boundaries aids me in crafting a secure life for myself.
4. My thoughts, body, and soul are my own.
5. Love and serenity envelop my interactions and choices today.
6. I exchange animosity, fury, and turmoil with deliberate and positive connections.
7. I let go of the sensation of solitude.
8. I release the emotions of guilt, pain, and shame.
9. My experiences of abuse and trauma do not define my identity.
10. Despite my current pain, I genuinely and wholeheartedly love and embrace myself.

Take a deep breath. Your journey to healing begins here. Together, we will explore exercises and uncover the layers of your past, strengthen your inner self, and light the path toward a brighter, more emotionally resilient future.

With warmth, empathy, and unwavering support,
Leigh W. Hart

UNDERSTANDING YOUR INNER CHILD

Children who try to be good enough to win their parents' love have no way of knowing that unconditional love cannot be bought with conditional behavior.

— LINDSAY C. GIBSON

Understanding your inner child is like shining a light on the roots of a tree; it allows you to comprehend the foundation upon which your emotional and relational experiences have been built.

As you start this exploration, let me start by posing a thought-provoking question: How might your quest for love and acceptance in childhood be influencing your current relationships and self-esteem? Take a moment to reflect on this. It's not an easy question, and the answers may not immediately surface, but they hold the key to unlocking profound personal growth and emotional resilience.

Your inner child is that part of you that carries the memories, emotions, and beliefs from your earliest years. It's the inner echo of your childhood experiences, both the joyful and the painful ones. Understanding and connecting with your inner child is a key step in the process of reparenting yourself—the act of providing the care, love, and validation you may have missed as a child.

In the following pages, let's discuss why understanding your inner child is so vital for your mental health and personal growth.

Your inner child isn't some abstract concept; it's a living presence within you. It's the part of you that experienced the world with innocence, vulnerability, and boundless curiosity. It's also the part of you that may have endured pain, neglect, or rejection, leaving behind scars that continue to affect your life today. By reconnecting with your inner child, you open the door to healing these wounds, providing the love and acceptance you may have missed in your formative years.

The significance of understanding your inner child lies in the fact that it directly impacts your current relationships, your self-esteem, and your overall emotional well-being. It shapes the way you relate to others, how you handle conflicts, and the choices you make in your life. Unresolved issues from your past can manifest as emotional triggers and patterns of behavior that hinder your growth and fulfillment as an adult.

But the good news is that by embracing your inner child with warmth, compassion, and understanding, you can rewrite the script of your life. You can break free from the limitations and repetitive cycles that have held you back and cultivate a healthier relationship with yourself and others. You can learn to regulate your emotions more effectively and build a stronger sense of self.

The process of understanding your inner child is an act of self-love and self-discovery. It may require some courage and self-reflection, but it also offers the promise of profound transformation and growth.

Let's begin with an open heart and a commitment to nurturing the most vulnerable parts of ourselves—our inner child.

INTRODUCTION TO THE CONCEPT OF THE INNER CHILD

Our inner child can play into our everyday life without us even being aware of it. Let's look at an example.

Charlie's Story

I used to feel like I was walking on eggshells, constantly fearing criticism from others. It didn't matter if it was my boss giving constructive feedback at work, my mom pointing out my flaws, or my spouse expressing disappointment in me. The moment I heard any form of criticism, I'd be overwhelmed with a suffocating sense of shame, feeling utterly useless and worthless. It was like a switch in my mind, and I'd spiral into a dark place where I believed I could never be good enough for anyone, including myself, eventually leading to depression.

After years of enduring this crippling pattern, I reached a breaking point and decided it was time to seek help. I immersed myself in therapy, hoping to find some answers and learn how to cope with these overwhelming feelings of inadequacy.

During my therapy sessions, the therapist delved deep into my past and asked me about my inner child. At first, it seemed like an odd question. What did my childhood have to do with my current struggles? But I trusted the process and began exploring my inner world.

I unearthed painful memories from my childhood. I realized that, as a young boy, I had never truly felt supported. The expectations placed on me were clear–don't show emotion, never cry, and never reveal fear. I was repeatedly told to "suck it up" and be a provider, to be strong and stoic. If I ever did cry or show vulnerability, I was met with ridicule and name-calling, labeled as a "softy" or a "baby."

In those moments of self-exploration, I connected with that young boy within me who had been denied the right to express his feelings and fears. I could see how this lack of support had carried over into my adult life, manifesting as an intense fear of criticism and a belief that I was inherently flawed.

But something incredible happened during my therapy journey. I started to offer that young, wounded boy the support and understanding he had never received. I allowed him to express his emotions, cry if needed, and confront his fears. It was like extending a compassionate hand to my own inner child, telling him that he was worthy of love and support, just as he was.

As I nurtured and healed that wounded inner child, I began to notice profound changes in my adult self. The crippling fear of criticism slowly started to lose its grip on me. I found myself becoming more resilient in the face of constructive feedback, and I no longer saw it as a reflection of my worth. Instead, I saw it as an opportunity for growth and improvement. The journey was not easy, but it was transformative.

The Psychological Theory Behind the Inner Child

Let's dive into the heart of the matter—understanding the psychological theory behind the inner child and how it influences your adult behaviors and emotions. The term "inner child" represents the connection you have within yourself to your child self and your childhood memories. This inner child is not something separate from you; it's a part of who you are today.

Think of it as a little version of yourself, carrying all the experiences, emotions, and memories from your early years. These experiences shape the lens through which you view the world and influence how you react to various situations as an adult.

Now, here's where it gets interesting—those behaviors and emotions you sometimes find yourself grappling with as an adult often mirror those you experienced as a child. This can lead to distress, confusion, and frustration as you try to navigate the complexities of the adult world. You might wonder why you react in certain ways, struggle with certain issues, or feel stuck in patterns that seem beyond your control.

The inner child is like a little guardian of your past, whispering in your ear and reminding you of those old wounds, beliefs, and unmet needs. It's not about blaming your child self or dwelling in the past, but rather understanding that these childhood experiences continue to play a role in your present-day life.

The impact of your inner child on your adult behaviors and emotions can be profound. It can show up in your relationships, career, self-esteem, and overall emotional well-being.

The journey of inner child work is intense, difficult, and can feel isolating. I am here to let you know you are not alone. I want to share two stories with you that you may be able to relate to.

Alesa's Story

When Alesa first entered therapy group, she carried with her a notebook filled with the daunting "work" that awaited her. This notebook served as her shield, protecting her from the pain and vulnerability she knew she would have to confront. Much like in her early years, Alesa had learned to carry the weight of her own needs, always putting others before herself and apologizing for things that didn't require an apology. She had become skilled at leaning out because leaning in meant the risk of abandonment, being deemed "too much," going hungry, and feeling deprived.

As children, we often adapt to our circumstances by protecting ourselves emotionally. Over time, this protection becomes our armor, and it can be so all-encompassing that we lose the ability to feel even a simple hug. Our adult relationships may mirror these childhood patterns, with us either seeking out overly avoidant or overly needy partners. Trusting our instincts becomes difficult, and sometimes, we unconsciously burden our own children with our emotional needs.

But here's where the transformation begins—when we muster the courage to face our wounds, acknowledge our protective armor, and ask ourselves, "Now what?" Alesa, in her remarkable journey, invited her entire family into this space, including her younger self, younger Alesa. With empathy, love, compassion, and nurturing, she addressed the pain of her past. She confronted the neglect, the hunger, the absence of proper birthday celebrations, and the inherent unfairness of it all.

And guess what? It is unfair. Children should naturally get to be children, nourished, loved, and cared for. By addressing her pain with kindness and love, Alesa began to rewrite the narrative. She reassured her inner child that there is, indeed, enough —for everyone, including herself.

This doesn't mean our patterns magically disappear. They linger, but when they resurface, we can gently pat our own arm and say, "There, there, little one. I've got you. There is enough." This, my dear readers, is the first step in reparenting our inner child. This is the essence of resilience. We acknowledge our wounds, and we allow others to witness them. It's in this vulnerability that true healing begins.

Human connection is the cornerstone of healing. We don't need masses of people; we just need one person who truly sees us for who we are. The journey doesn't end with one breakthrough in therapy; it continues, unfolds, and evolves. So, let me leave you with Alesa's own words on how she is currently reparenting her wounded inner child.

"I now keep a picture of little Alesa on my desk, on my phone, and close to my heart. Whenever she appears, which happens quite often, I make a conscious effort to truly see her. I close my eyes and envision her bouncy, messy hair, her freckles, and how she used to hide behind things when she was scared. I find myself missing her, so I take a moment to breathe her in, sit with her, and reassure her of everything she needs to hear. I let her know that I understand her and that her feelings are valid. Sometimes, I share laughter with her, and sometimes, I shed tears. Each time, it alters my perception of how grown up Alesa is in that particular moment."

THE EGO AND THE INNER CHILD

Let's begin with an essential piece of the puzzle: understanding the role of the ego in safeguarding your inner child. The ego, often misunderstood, is like the protector of your inner child, standing guard over the precious treasure within you. It's time to shed light on this relationship.

Think of your ego as a dedicated guardian, always vigilant and ready to shield your inner child from perceived threats. Its intentions are noble, aiming to keep you safe and secure. But here's the twist: the ego can sometimes go overboard, inadvertently causing more harm than good.

Your ego's knee-jerk reaction to perceived threats is to retaliate. It's like a loyal soldier in your inner army, defending your inner child at all costs. However, there's a catch: this retaliation often takes the form of unhealthy coping mechanisms and behaviors.

Imagine someone says something hurtful, and your ego jumps in to protect your inner child. But instead of using gentleness, it might employ harsh words, defensiveness, or even denial. It may appear that your ego is doing your inner child a favor, but in reality, it's suppressing their true feelings and stifling their creativity and self-expression.

The Suppression Game

When your ego gets too zealous in its protective role, it inadvertently suppresses your inner child's authentic emotions and needs. Your inner child's voice becomes muffled, and their creativity gets smothered under layers of defense mechanisms. The result? You may find yourself stuck in a cycle of unhealthy behaviors and emotional turmoil.

But fear not, for awareness is the first step toward change. Developing a healthier relationship between your ego and inner child is key. The ability to recognize when the ego's protective measures are doing more harm than good will make all the difference.

Inner child versus ego: Let's have a look at the difference.

Inner Child	Ego
Lives within you	Resides in your mind
Where the record plays	A record of your past
Takes refuge behind the ego	Job is to protect the inner child
The wounded, fearful version of you	Masked version of you
Believes the truth of these stories	Makes up stories to suppress inner child's feelings
Reacts based on ego response	Reacts to your inner child based on internal programs
Feels safe when fully aware	Feels safe when unaware
Needs to release emotions	Wants to suppress emotions

Remember that healing your wounded inner child is not about casting blame on your ego. Instead, it's about nurturing a compassionate alliance between your ego and inner child. It's about learning to soothe your inner child's pain in a healthier, more constructive way.

REPARENTING YOUR WOUNDED INNER CHILD

If you've taken the first step by reading my first book in this series, *Reparenting Your Wounded Inner Child*, you've already started your courageous path of self-discovery and healing. This companion workbook is designed to take you further, to help you delve deeper into your inner world, connect more strongly with your inner child, and cultivate a loving and nurturing relationship with yourself.

Here are the key highlights of reparenting your wounded inner child that I'll be building upon in this workbook:

- **Understanding the past:** The foundation of inner child healing is gaining insight into your past experiences and their impact on your present life. We'll continue to explore your childhood experiences, uncovering any hidden wounds and emotional baggage that may still be affecting you.

- **Self-compassion:** Reparenting is all about self-compassion. It's about recognizing that your inner child deserves love, care, and understanding. We'll delve deeper into self-compassion practices, teaching you to be kind and gentle with yourself, just as you would with a wounded child.

- **Emotional awareness:** Building emotional intelligence is crucial for inner child healing. You'll learn to identify, validate, and express your emotions in healthy ways. I will help you connect how your inner child's wounds are impacting your daily life and provide practical exercises to help you connect with your feelings and understand their origins.

- **Attachment and connection:** A secure attachment to your inner child is crucial for the process of reparenting. By nurturing this connection, I will lead you through a series of exercises designed to strengthen this bond. These exercises will empower you to consistently and lovingly support yourself, fostering a deep sense of self-care and compassion.

- **Healing through exercises:** This workbook is not just about theory; it's about practical steps for change. You'll find a variety of exercises and activities that will enable you to apply what you've learned in a hands-on way.

These exercises will empower you to nurture your inner child actively.

- **Self-reflection:** Self-awareness is a fundamental aspect of CBT for inner child healing. By engaging in journaling and self-reflection exercises, individuals can delve into their thoughts, beliefs, and behavioral patterns, leading to increased clarity and insight into their inner world.
- **Growth and transformation:** These are the ultimate goals of reparenting. Through the process of connecting with your inner child and healing past wounds, you will unlock your true potential and pave the way for a brighter future.

EXERCISE: ASSESSING YOUR CURRENT STATE

Let's get started with a crucial exercise to assess your current relationship with your inner child.

Remember, this assessment is not about judgment but about gaining awareness and understanding of where you are right now. Be gentle with yourself as you go through this process, and know that change is possible.

Step 1: Find a Quiet Space

Before starting, locate a comfortable and peaceful area where you can be undisturbed. Take several deep breaths and focus on the present moment. This activity demands your complete attention, so be fully present and receptive.

Step 2: Self-Reflection

Think about your relationship with your inner child. Ask yourself these questions, take your time to answer them honestly, and circle the answer below:

How often do I acknowledge the presence of my inner child in my life?

(Rarely,   Occasionally,   Often,   Always)

Do I treat my inner child with kindness and compassion?

(Rarely,   Occasionally,   Often,   Always)

Am I aware of the wounds from my past that affect my inner child?

(Not at all,   Somewhat,   Moderately,   Fully aware)

Do I actively work on healing and nurturing my inner child?

(Not at all,   Occasionally,   Sometimes,   Consistently)

How do I react when my inner child's needs or emotions surface?

(Neglect,   Ignore,   Reject,   Acknowledge,   Comfort)

Am I able to set healthy boundaries to protect my inner child from harm?

(Never,   Rarely,   Sometimes,   Always)

Step 3: Reflect on Your Responses

Take a moment to look at your responses. This exercise is about self-awareness, and there are no right or wrong answers. It's essential to be honest with yourself about where you currently stand in your relationship with your inner child. This should allow you to gauge where you can begin, what areas need work, and what areas you are comfortable with.

_____
_____
_____
_____
_____

Step 4: Set Intentions

Now, consider where you'd like your relationship with your inner child to be. Write down a few intentions or goals for your inner child healing journey. These could be things like:

- "I intend to acknowledge my inner child's presence and needs daily."
- "I will treat my inner child with kindness and compassion, just as I would with a real child."

- "I am committed to understanding and healing the wounds from my past that affect my inner child."

_____

_____

_____

_____

_____

Step 5: Take Action

Remember, healing and reparenting your inner child require consistent effort and self-compassion. Take your intentions and turn them into actionable steps. What can you do today, this week, or this month to start improving your relationship with your inner child?

_____

_____

_____

_____

_____

EXERCISE: GETTING TO KNOW YOUR INNER CHILD

In this exercise, we will take the first step in building a strong connection with your inner child. Your inner child holds the key to healing and transformation, and by getting to know them, you'll pave the way for a healthier and more fulfilling life.

Step 1: Find a Quiet and Comfortable Space

Find a tranquil location where you can be undisturbed for a while. Get into a comfortable sitting or lying position and take a few deep breaths to relax your mind and center yourself. If you have a photo of yourself as a child, I invite you to bring it with you into this space.

Step 2: Close Your Eyes and Imagine

Close your eyes and envision a tranquil and stunning location. It might be a beach, your comfy bed, your favorite vacation spot, or any place that brings you a sense of safety and peace. Picture yourself in this setting.

Step 3: Invite Your Inner Child

Imagine a small, vulnerable, and innocent version of yourself standing in front of you in this serene place. This is your inner child. They may look like you did when you were around five to seven years old. Approach your inner child with a warm and welcoming smile.

Step 4: Start a Conversation

Engage in a gentle conversation with your inner child. Ask them questions like:

- How are you feeling at the moment?"
- Is there something I can offer to make you feel better?

- What is your favorite color?
- Do you like to play games?
- What makes you happy or sad?
- Is there anything you want to share with me?

As you converse with your inner child, pay close attention to their responses, feelings, and needs. Be patient, and let the conversation flow naturally.

Step 5: Listen With Empathy

Listen to your inner child with empathy and without judgment. Validate their feelings and experiences. Remember, your inner child might carry pain, fear, or unmet needs from the past. Your role is to provide a safe and loving space for them to express themselves.

Step 6: Promise to Nurture and Protect

Make a heartfelt promise to your inner child that you will always be there for them, just as a loving parent would. Promise to nurture, protect, and support them through the journey of healing. Say the words, "I love you."

Step 7: Journal Your Experience

After the conversation with your inner child, take some time to write down your experience. Reflect on what you learned, the emotions that came up, and any insights you gained. This will serve as a valuable resource as you continue your inner child healing journey.

Step 8: Repeat Regularly

Getting to know your inner child is an ongoing process. Commit to repeating this exercise regularly, ideally daily or at least a few times a week. The more you connect with your inner child, the stronger your bond will become and the more healing and transformation you'll experience.

Remember, your inner child is a part of you that deserves love, care, and attention. By getting to know them and building a nurturing relationship, you're taking the first step toward reparenting your wounded inner child and creating a brighter future for yourself. Keep up the good work, and don't forget to be kind and patient with yourself throughout this journey.

INNER CHILD JOURNAL PROMPTS

You will find these prompts at the end of each chapter. The goal is to encourage self-reflection and active engagement in the healing process. Let's dive in:

- **The nurturing guardian:** Imagine you are the loving guardian of your wounded inner child. Write a letter of unconditional love and support to that child, reassuring them that you're here to protect and nurture them. What would you say to comfort your inner child?

_____

_____

_____

_____

_____

_____

_____

_____

_____

- **Parental messages:** Recall messages or phrases that your caregivers often repeated during your childhood. Write down these messages, and then analyze how they have influenced your self-perception and behavior.

Which messages would you like to challenge or reframe?

1. _____
2. _____
3. _____
4. _____
5. _____

- **Embracing vulnerability:** Explore moments in your life when you felt vulnerable or exposed. How did you react? Did you suppress your feelings, or did you express them? Reflect on how allowing yourself to be vulnerable can be a powerful step toward healing your inner child.

_____
_____
_____
_____
_____

- **Unmet needs:** Identify unmet emotional needs from your childhood, such as validation, attention, or affection. Describe how these unmet needs have affected your adult life. How can you begin to fulfill these needs for your inner child now?

_____

_____

_____

_____

_____

- **Inner child's dreams:** Think back to your childhood dreams and aspirations. Were there any talents or interests that you abandoned? Reconnect with those dreams and consider how you can reintegrate them into your life today.

_____

_____

_____

_____

_____

In this chapter, we've traveled back in time, exploring the roots of our emotional wounds and getting to know the little version of ourselves that still resides within. You've shown incredible strength by facing your past and acknowledging the pain that may have been buried for far too long.

Now that we have a deeper understanding of our wounded inner child, it's time to take this journey a step further. We're about to embark on a path that will lead us toward healing and transformation, and understanding the foundation of Cognitive Behavioral Therapy will be our trusty guide.

FOUNDATIONS OF COGNITIVE BEHAVIORAL THERAPY

It takes courage to grow up and become who you really are.

— E.E. CUMMINGS

As you follow the journey of inner child healing, it's important to equip yourself with the right tools and knowledge to pave the way for transformation. This chapter is a stepping stone in your quest to reparent and heal your wounded inner child, and it's all about the foundations of Cognitive Behavioral Therapy (CBT).

CBT is a powerful therapeutic approach, and it's not just for therapists and psychologists. In fact, it's something you can use to bring about profound changes in your life, starting today. So, let's dive in together, explore the core principles of CBT, and understand how these techniques can be applied to nurture and heal your inner child.

As we journey through this chapter, I want you to ponder this question: In what ways might embracing your authentic self challenge the beliefs and behaviors you developed in childhood?

This question is at the heart of our exploration because it's a critical starting point. Your authentic self is the real you, buried beneath the layers of conditioning, coping mechanisms, and adaptations that were born in your early years. Embracing your authentic self is like uncovering a precious gem hidden beneath layers of sediment. It's a journey of self-discovery and self-acceptance, but it's also a path that challenges the very beliefs and behaviors that have shaped your life until now.

Our inner child often holds onto beliefs and behaviors that were formed in response to past experiences, especially those rooted in childhood. These beliefs and behaviors, while once protective, may now limit your potential for growth, happiness, and healthy relationships. Welcoming your authentic self means confronting these patterns and reshaping them to align with the person you want to become.

By the end of this chapter, you can expect to have a clearer under-standing of how CBT can be a catalyst for change in your life, leading to enhanced self-awareness and emotional well-being.

So, let's take this step together as we continue on a journey of self-discovery and inner child healing. The foundation we lay here will serve as the bedrock for the profound changes you're about to experience.

BASIC AND ADVANCED PRINCIPLES OF CBT

CBT is like a beacon of hope in the storm of life's challenges. It's a psychological treatment that has proven its worth time and time again. It's not just some trendy fad–it's a powerhouse for tackling a wide range of issues, from depression and anxiety to substance abuse and relationship problems.

Cognitive Behavioral Therapy (CBT) is a pragmatic, brief type of psychotherapy that assists individuals in acquiring skills and tactics to foster and maintain mental well-being. It centers on the current moment and the challenges encountered in everyday life, encouraging individuals to assess their interpretations of events and their impact on emotions.

CBT is:

- organized
- time-limited
- problem-oriented and goal-focused
- teaches tangible skills and solutions

Studies upon studies have shown that CBT works wonders, improving your overall functioning and quality of life. In fact, it's often just as effective, if not more so, than other therapies or even psychiatric medications (David et al., 2018). We're talking about the gold standard of talk therapy right here!

CBT doesn't just treat symptoms; it digs deep to address the root causes of your struggles. It's not a magic pill, but it's a powerful tool to have in your toolbox for inner healing.

THE HISTORY OF CBT

Okay, let's take a little trip back in time. CBT didn't just appear out of thin air. It's been honed and refined over the years.

The Birth of Behavioral Therapy

You know, when it comes to helping people with their mental struggles, we've been at it for quite some time. Back in the early 1900s, pioneers like Pavlov, Skinner, and Watson were cooking up some interesting ideas. They believed that behaviors could be measured, understood, and changed. They laid the foundation for what we now call behavioral therapy (Morrow, 2022).

Now, fast forward to the 1930s and 40s, right around the time World War II was happening. Many brave veterans were returning home, but they were carrying emotional baggage. They needed help, and they needed it fast. That's when the first wave of behavioral therapy came into play. Researchers were busy studying how people learn to behave and react in different situations. This fresh approach offered a quicker and more effective way to treat issues like depression and anxiety, as opposed to the lengthy psychoanalysis of the time (Morrow, 2022).

The Rise of Cognitive Therapy

Jump ahead to the 1950s, and you've got a maverick psychologist named Albert Ellis. He was all about thoughts, feelings, and behaviors. He introduced something called rational emotive behavior therapy (REBT). Essentially, Ellis believed that our emotional distress doesn't come from the events themselves but from how we think about those events. It was a game-changer (Morrow, 2022).

Around the same time, another brilliant mind, Aaron T. Beck, was working with depressed clients. He noticed a common thread—they all had these negative views about themselves, others, and the future. No matter how much they dug into their past, those negative views stuck like glue. Beck's lightbulb moment led to the birth of cognitive therapy. He realized that the thoughts that pop up in our heads, which he called "automatic thoughts," had a huge impact on how we feel. By challenging and changing these negative thoughts, people could experience real and lasting change. It's like giving your mind a makeover (Morrow, 2022)!

The Marriage of Behavioral and Cognitive Therapies

Now, here's where it gets interesting. In the 1960s, researchers started digging even deeper into how thoughts affect our behaviors and emotions. They called it the "cognitive revolution." It highlighted just how crucial our conscious thinking is in therapy (Morrow, 2022).

As time went on, behavioral therapy had already proven its worth in treating issues like phobias and anxiety. Cognitive therapy was on the rise, too. Therapists realized they could blend the best of both worlds. They started using behavioral techniques along with cognitive approaches to tackle various disorders. Both these schools of thought might have different focuses, but they share a common ground—helping individuals in the present moment. It's all about what's happening here and now.

BASIC PRINCIPLES OF CBT

Before we dive into the more complex aspects of CBT, let's establish a strong foundation by understanding its basic principles:

Thoughts

Our thoughts act as the filter through which we view the world, significantly influencing our emotional state and actions. In the context of inner child healing, it's crucial to recognize that the way we think about ourselves, others, and our experiences can either empower us or hinder our progress.

Understanding the Power of Thoughts:

- Thoughts are not merely random or inconsequential. They shape our perception of reality and can influence our self-esteem, self-worth, and self-concept.

- Negative or distorted thoughts can lead to self-doubt, anxiety, and depression, making it challenging to heal our inner child wounds.

The Inner Dialogue:

- We all have an inner dialogue, a continuous stream of thoughts that often go unnoticed. CBT encourages us to become aware of this dialogue and the messages we're sending ourselves.
- By paying attention to our self-talk, we can identify patterns of negative or self-critical thinking that may be rooted in past experiences.

Changing Your Thoughts:

- CBT teaches us to challenge and reframe unhelpful thoughts. This means questioning the accuracy and validity of our negative beliefs about ourselves and replacing them with more balanced and constructive perspectives.
- Through cognitive restructuring techniques, you'll learn to transform your inner dialogue, fostering greater self-compassion and self-empowerment.

Feelings

Emotions are a fundamental aspect of the human experience. They provide us with valuable information about how we are reacting to various situations and events. In the context of inner child healing, understanding and acknowledging our emotions are essential steps toward healing and personal growth.

Recognizing Emotions:

- CBT encourages us to recognize and name our emotions accurately. By doing so, we gain clarity about what we are feeling in different situations.
- This awareness allows us to distinguish between emotions, such as sadness, anger, fear, and joy, and understand their unique triggers.

The Connection Between Thoughts and Feelings:

- Our emotions are closely connected to our thoughts. Negative thoughts often lead to negative emotions, while positive and balanced thoughts can result in more positive emotional states.
- CBT helps us identify the thought patterns that contribute to specific emotional reactions.

Embracing Emotional Expression:

- It's crucial to acknowledge that all emotions, even the uncomfortable ones, serve a purpose. CBT encourages us to express our emotions in healthy ways rather than suppressing or denying them.

- By exploring and processing our emotions, we can release pent-up feelings, fostering emotional healing and resilience.

Behaviors

Our actions and behaviors are the outward manifestations of our thoughts and emotions. CBT emphasizes the interconnectedness of thoughts, feelings, and behaviors, recognizing that changing our actions can positively influence our inner world.

Recognizing Behavior Patterns:

- CBT invites us to examine our behaviors and identify any patterns that may be hindering our healing and personal growth. These patterns might include avoidance, self-sabotage, or unhealthy coping mechanisms.
- Recognizing these patterns is the initial move toward breaking away from them.

Taking Positive Actions:

- CBT encourages us to take deliberate and positive actions that align with our healing goals. These actions might involve establishing boundaries, engaging in self-care, or seeking assistance from others.
- By taking control of our behaviors, we can create a nurturing environment for our wounded inner child to heal and grow.

Now, let's dig a bit deeper into the fundamental principles of CBT:

- **Core beliefs:** These are deeply ingrained beliefs about ourselves, others, and the world around us. They often stem from early experiences and significantly influence our thoughts and behaviors.
- **Dysfunctional assumptions:** We all make assumptions, but some of these can be negative and limiting. CBT helps us identify and challenge these assumptions to create a more balanced perspective.
- **Automatic negative thoughts:** Often referred to as ANTs, these are those intrusive, critical, and self-defeating thoughts that pop into our minds automatically. CBT equips us with tools to intercept and reframe these thoughts.

Identifying the Principles of CBT

As we progress in our inner child healing journey, it's vital to grasp the overarching principles of CBT:

- **Individualized approach:** In your quest to heal your wounded inner child, it's crucial to understand that your experiences and needs are unique. CBT recognizes this individuality and tailors its techniques to fit your specific circumstances. This means that the journey is all about you, and the techniques we explore in this workbook will be customized to support your personal growth and healing.

- **Therapeutic alliance:** Just as in traditional therapy, the bond of trust and collaboration between you and this workbook is paramount. You are embarking on a journey of self-discovery and healing, and a strong therapeutic alliance is essential for success. Think of this workbook as your trusted companion, providing you with guidance, support, and empathy throughout your inner child healing process.

- **Active participation:** Healing your inner child requires your active involvement and engagement in the process. This workbook will offer exercises and activities that prompt you to delve deep into your emotions, thoughts, and behaviors. Your active participation is the driving force behind your progress, making it a truly transformative experience.

- **Goal-oriented:** CBT is known for its focus on specific goals and targeted problem-solving. As you work through this workbook, you will identify clear objectives for your healing journey. These goals will serve as guiding lights, helping you measure your progress and stay motivated as you overcome the challenges of inner child healing.

- **Present-centered:** While we will explore your past and the wounds of your inner child, CBT primarily emphasizes addressing your current thoughts and behaviors. This approach empowers you to make tangible changes in your life right now, gradually alleviating the impact of past trauma and fostering a stronger sense of self in the present.

- **Educative:** CBT aims to empower you with practical skills that enable you to become your own therapist. The tools and techniques you'll learn in this workbook are not just for immediate relief but are meant to equip you with the ability to navigate future challenges independently, fostering lasting personal growth and emotional resilience.

- **Time-limited:** Your inner child healing journey, with the help of this workbook, is designed to be efficient and effective. We respect your time and your commitment to healing, and we'll work diligently to make the most of your journey toward a healthier, more fulfilling life.

- **Structured sessions:** The workbook is structured to provide clarity and guidance throughout your healing process. Each session is carefully designed to build upon the previous one, creating a logical and progressive path toward inner child healing. This structure ensures that you have a roadmap to follow and that you can track your progress along the way.

- **Identifying, evaluating, and responding:** CBT will teach you how to recognize dysfunctional thoughts and patterns, assess their validity, and respond to them effectively. This skill will be invaluable as you work to heal your wounded inner child, allowing you to challenge and reframe negative beliefs that may have held you back for years.

- **Versatile techniques:** Throughout this workbook, we will explore a variety of methods and exercises to transform your thinking, mood, and behavior. This versatility ensures that you have a toolkit filled with strategies to address the unique challenges that may arise during your inner child healing journey.

By understanding and embracing these principles, you will be well-prepared to embark on a transformative journey of inner child healing, guided by the compassionate and empowering approach of CBT.

Complex Aspects of CBT

Cognitive restructuring is a powerful technique within CBT that helps you transform negative or distorted thought patterns into more balanced and constructive ones. It's a crucial step in healing your wounded inner child because it allows you to challenge and change the unhelpful beliefs that may have been holding you back.

Understanding Cognitive Restructuring:

- **Definition:** Cognitive restructuring involves identifying and challenging irrational or negative thoughts and replacing them with more accurate and positive ones. It helps you shift your perspective and develop healthier ways of thinking about yourself and your experiences.
- **Examples:** Imagine you often think, "I'm worthless and unlovable" due to past experiences. Cognitive restructuring would involve examining the evidence for and against this belief. You might find evidence that

contradicts this thought, such as supportive friends or achievements in your life. This process can help you reframe your belief to something like, "I am lovable and deserving of love."

Techniques for Cognitive Restructuring:

- **Identify automatic negative thoughts (ANTs):** Pay attention to the automatic negative thoughts that arise in your mind. These are often irrational and unhelpful, but they can be challenging to spot initially.
- **Challenge your thoughts:** Once you've identified an ANT, question its validity. Ask yourself if there is any evidence to support or refute the thought. Are there alternative explanations or perspectives?
- **Replace with balanced thoughts:** After challenging the negative thought, replace it with a more balanced and realistic one. This new thought should reflect a fair and compassionate view of yourself or the situation.
- **Practice affirmations:** Use positive affirmations to reinforce the new, healthier thoughts. Repeating affirmations can help rewire your brain to embrace more positive beliefs.
- **Journaling:** Keep a journal to track your thought patterns and the progress you make in restructuring your thinking. This can be a helpful way to monitor your growth.

Behavioral Experiments

Behavioral experiments are another vital component of CBT, designed to test and challenge your beliefs, assumptions, and behaviors. These experiments are practical and hands-on, allowing you to gather real-life evidence and gain a deeper understanding of your inner world.

Understanding Behavioral Experiments:

- **Definition:** Behavioral experiments involve actively trying out new behaviors or approaches in real-life situations to test the accuracy of your beliefs and thoughts. They help bridge the gap between theory and practice, offering concrete evidence to inform your cognitive restructuring.
- **Examples:** Let's say you have a fear of rejection and avoid social situations. A behavioral experiment could involve deliberately attending a social event and observing how people react to you. You might find that your fear of rejection is not as justified as you thought, as people are more accepting and welcoming than you anticipated.

Types of Behavioral Experiments:

- **Exposure experiments:** These involve gradually facing situations or triggers that cause anxiety or discomfort. By exposing yourself to these situations in a controlled manner, you can desensitize yourself to the fear or discomfort over time.

- **Behavioral activation:** This type of experiment focuses on increasing your engagement in enjoyable and meaningful activities, even when you don't initially feel like doing them. It helps improve your mood and motivation.
- **Social experiments:** These experiments involve testing your beliefs about how others perceive you by interacting with people and gauging their reactions.

Steps to Conduct Behavioral Experiments (*Using Behavioral, 2020*):

- **Identify a belief:** Choose a specific belief or assumption that you want to test through an experiment. For example, if you believe that you're unlikable, you might want to test this belief in a social context.
- **Plan the experiment:** Develop a clear plan for the experiment, including what you will do, where and when it will happen, and how you will measure the results.
- **Conduct the experiment:** Follow through with your plan, paying attention to your thoughts, emotions, and behaviors throughout the process. Document your experiences.
- **Evaluate the results:** After completing the experiment, analyze the outcomes objectively. Did the results

support or challenge your initial belief? What did you learn from the experience?

- **Adjust and iterate:** Use the insights gained from the experiment to adjust your beliefs and behaviors as needed. If necessary, repeat the experiment to reinforce the learning.

By incorporating cognitive restructuring and behavioral experiments into your inner child healing journey, you'll be better equipped to challenge and change the negative thought patterns and behaviors that have held you back for so long.

CBT AND THE INNER CHILD

So, how can CBT guide you in healing your wounded inner child? CBT is a powerful approach that can work wonders when it comes to addressing those deep-seated issues and emotional wounds from the past. It's like a gentle but firm hand guiding you toward a healthier and happier you. Let's explore some of the specific ways in which CBT can help you on your healing journey and the techniques that will be your allies in this process.

Cognitive Restructuring

This is all about challenging and changing those negative thought patterns that have been ingrained since your early years. By identifying and replacing those old, limiting beliefs with new, empowering ones, you're essentially rewriting the script of your inner dialogue. It's like giving your inner child a new, more supportive voice to listen to.

Exposure Therapy

Facing your fears and painful memories head-on can be daunting, but it's an essential part of healing. Exposure therapy, in this context, allows you to confront those past traumas gradually, helping you build resilience and desensitize the emotional charge attached to them. It's a bit like holding your inner child's hand as you both take small steps toward healing.

Guided Discovery

CBT encourages you to become an active investigator of your own thoughts, feelings, and behaviors. Through guided discovery, you'll learn to uncover the roots of your emotional responses and why your inner child reacts the way it does. This self-awareness is like a flashlight in the dark, helping you understand and make sense of your past and present.

Journaling

Grab a notebook because journaling is your trusty sidekick in this journey. By regularly recording your thoughts and feelings, you can identify patterns and triggers. It can help you dissect those automatic negative thoughts and replace them with healthier alternatives. It's like giving your inner child a safe space to express itself and process emotions.

Behavioral Experiments

Healing your inner child isn't just about changing your thoughts; it's also about changing your actions. CBT encourages you to take small steps towards facing your fears or challenging your old patterns. These behavioral experiments help your inner child learn that it's safe to try new things and that change is possible.

Relaxation and Stress Reduction Techniques

Healing can be emotionally taxing, so it's essential to have relaxation and stress reduction techniques in your toolbox. These methods, like deep breathing, mindfulness, or meditation, are like a warm hug for your inner child, helping it feel safe and secure even in the face of difficult emotions.

Successive Approximation

Sometimes, healing is a gradual process, like climbing a staircase one step at a time. Successive approximation encourages you to set achievable goals and celebrate each small victory along the way. It's a reminder that healing is a journey, not a destination, and your inner child deserves praise for every step taken.

Incorporating these CBT techniques into your inner child healing journey will not only help you understand the past but also actively engage in the process of change. Remember, healing your inner child takes time and effort, but the rewards are profound: a healthier relationship with yourself and others, improved emotional regulation, and a stronger sense of self. These tools are not just for the moment; they're for ongoing personal growth and emotional resilience.

EXERCISE: EXPLORING YOUR INNER CHILD'S NEEDS

In this first exercise, we're going to explore the needs of your wounded inner child. By doing so, you'll gain insight into the core issues that have affected your emotional well-being. Remember, this process can be both enlightening and challenging, but it's a crucial step toward healing and reparenting your inner child.

- Locate a tranquil and cozy area where you can work without interruptions.
- Close your eyes, breathe deeply, and envision yourself as a child. Imagine yourself as a young child, maybe around four to six years old. What did you look like? What was your environment like? Try to vividly bring this memory to life in your mind.
- Now, in this child's shoes, think about what you needed the most back then. What were your emotional needs, your desires, and your fears? Write down these needs using phrases like "I needed to feel safe," "I needed to be heard," or "I needed to be valued and protected."
- Take your time with this. Be honest and compassionate with yourself. You might uncover painful memories or

emotions, and that's okay. Allow yourself to feel whatever comes up.

_____

_____

_____

_____

_____

- Next, transition into your adult self. Reflect on how these unmet childhood needs may still be affecting your adult life and relationships. Write down any patterns or behaviors that you recognize as a result of these unmet needs. For example, do you still find yourself in need of protection? Do you still feel you are not being valued?

_____

_____

_____

_____

_____

- Now, consider how you can start meeting these needs for yourself today. What can you do to provide the love, safety, and support that your inner child needs? Write down specific actions or strategies you can implement. For example, if you are in need of worth, you could start a self-care routine. If you feel the need for love, you could work on reparenting techniques.

_____

_____

_____

_____

_____

EXERCISE: REFRAMING UNHELPFUL THOUGHT PATTERNS

In this exercise, we will use CBT principles to help you identify and challenge negative thought patterns that may be holding you back from healing your inner child. This is a powerful tool for promoting self-awareness and positive change.

- Find a peaceful area to complete this exercise.
- Begin by thinking about a specific situation or trigger that often leads to negative emotions or self-criticism in your life. It could be an event, a person, or a recurring thought.
- Write down the automatic negative thoughts (ANTs) that arise when you think about this situation. These are the unhelpful, irrational, or critical thoughts that pop into your mind without conscious effort. An example could be, "I messed up that report at work, and I am going to get fired; I am useless!"

_____

_____

_____

_____

_____

- For each negative thought, ask yourself these questions:

  ○ Is this thought based on facts and evidence, or is it a distortion or assumption?

_____

_____

_____

_____

_____

  ○ What is the worst that could happen if this thought were true? Is that outcome realistic?

_____

_____

_____

_____

_____

  ○ Can I identify any cognitive distortions in this thought (e.g., black-and-white thinking, catastrophizing, person-alization)?

_____

_____

_____

- Challenge each negative thought with more balanced, rational, and compassionate alternatives. Write down these alternative thoughts and be as specific and logical as possible.

_____

_____

_____

_____

- Practice using these alternative thoughts whenever the triggering situation arises. This may take some time and repetition, but it's a powerful way to rewire your thought patterns and respond more positively to challenging situations.

INNER CHILD JOURNAL PROMPTS

You will find these prompts at the end of each chapter. The goal is to encourage self-reflection and active engagement in the healing process. Let's begin:

- **Healing symbols:** Reflect on any symbols or objects that represent your inner child's wounds and healing.

Draw or describe these symbols and explain their significance in your journey toward inner child healing.

- **Timeline of transformation:** Create a timeline of your life, marking significant moments or events that have impacted your inner child. Next to each event, write down how it has influenced your beliefs and emotions. Identify turning points or opportunities for healing.

- **Revisiting childhood dreams:** Recall a dream or aspiration you had as a child. Write about how it made you feel and why you may have abandoned it. Explore ways to reconnect with that inner child's dream and consider how pursuing it now can be a form of healing.

_____

_____

_____

_____

_____

- **The inner child's playlist:** Create a playlist of songs
  that resonate with your inner child's emotions. Include
  songs that bring up memories, feelings, or even songs
  you loved as a child. Listen to this playlist and journal
  about the emotions it stirs within you.

In this chapter, we explored the foundational principles of CBT
as a powerful framework for inner child healing. We delved
into the importance of understanding the core beliefs and
thought patterns developed during childhood, which continue
to influence our adult lives. As we transition into the next chapter, we will embark on a journey to uncover the layers of childhood trauma and generational trauma, shedding light on the
profound impact they have on our emotional well-being.
Through the integration of CBT techniques and a deeper
exploration of our past, we will gain valuable insights and tools
to begin the transformative process of healing and self-
discovery.

UNCOVERING CHILDHOOD AND GENERATIONAL TRAUMAS

So, like a forgotten fire, a childhood can always flare up again within us.

— GASTON BACHELARD

Our childhood experiences shape us in ways we may not fully comprehend until we shine a light on them. Unresolved childhood traumas can influence our decisions, our relationships, and even our emotional responses. To truly heal and grow, we must excavate those hidden treasures of pain, bringing them into the light of our consciousness.

Generational traumas, too, have a profound impact. They are the silent echoes of our ancestors' struggles, echoing through the generations. These patterns can unwittingly guide our actions and reactions, holding us hostage to the past unless we recognize and break the cycle.

This chapter is your guide, your compass, and your confidant on this journey. Here, we will explore the roots of your trauma, both in your own childhood and within your family's history. We will uncover the threads that connect your past to your present and empower you to make choices based on awareness rather than reactivity.

Ask yourself, what forgotten aspects of your childhood might still be influencing your life today?

Allow this question to guide you as you dive into the depths of your memories and emotions, for it is through this introspection that you will discover the roots of your inner child's pain. As you reflect on your answer, remember that this is not a journey of blame or judgment but a path of self-compassion and transformation.

IDENTIFYING SOURCES OF TRAUMA

Trauma can wear many disguises and take various forms. It's essential to recognize that everyone's experiences are unique. So, let's begin by introducing the concept that trauma comes in different shapes and sizes.

Understanding Trauma Responses

Trauma responses are your body's natural reactions to stressful or traumatic situations. Understanding these responses is crucial as they often shape how you react to life's challenges. Here are some common trauma responses (Sauber Millacci, 2023):

- **Fight:** You might find yourself becoming confrontational or aggressive in response to a threat, whether real or perceived.
- **Flight:** You may have a tendency to avoid situations or people that remind you of past trauma, trying to escape from distressing memories.
- **Freeze:** In this state, you might feel paralyzed, unable to move or respond to a situation. It's like hitting a mental "pause" button.
- **Fawn:** Some people adopt a people-pleasing attitude as a survival mechanism, always putting others' needs before their own.
- **Fright:** This response can leave you in a constant state of hyperarousal, making it difficult to relax and often leading to anxiety or panic attacks.
- **Flag:** Your body might signal distress through physical symptoms, like chronic pain or illness, which can be tied to unresolved trauma.
- **Faint:** You might experience dissociation or a sense of detachment from your body, emotions, or surroundings during traumatic events.

Common Examples of Trauma

Experiencing something traumatic can deeply impact your life, altering your thoughts, emotions, and daily experiences.

Defining trauma can be challenging, as it encompasses a wide range of potentially distressing events. What truly matters is not the event itself but rather how it affected you. Trauma can be best understood as any experience that overwhelms your thoughts, emotions, or body. It's a deeply personal journey, as your recollection of an event may differ significantly from someone else's experience of the same occurrence.

Let's explore 12 of the most common types of traumatic experiences (Mitts, 2019):

- **Verbal or emotional abuse:** Persistent insults, humiliation, or manipulation can leave lasting emotional scars.
- **Physical or sexual abuse:** Experiencing physical or sexual violence can deeply wound your inner child.
- **Neglect as a child:** Not receiving the love, care, and attention you need during childhood can be traumatic.
- **Spiritual or religious abuse:** Abusive practices or beliefs within religious or spiritual communities can cause emotional harm.
- **Accidents or natural disasters:** Surviving a car accident or going through a natural disaster can be a source of trauma.
- **Physical attack or assault:** Being a victim of violence can leave you with both physical and emotional trauma.
- **Witnessing domestic abuse or violence:** Seeing violence within your own home can be profoundly distressing.

- **Witnessing bodily harm or death:** Witnessing someone getting hurt or dying can be traumatic.
- **Sudden or violent death in your life:** The loss of a loved one through unexpected or violent means can be extremely traumatic.
- **Witnessing community violence:** Living in a high-crime area or experiencing community violence can leave lasting scars.
- **Fear of harm or high-stress environment:** Constantly feeling on edge or unsafe can be traumatic over time.
- **Exposure to school violence:** Being a victim of bullying or experiencing violence at school can have long-lasting effects.

The Three Steps to Identify Trauma

Step 1: Acknowledge What Hurts

The first step involves gently acknowledging the pain that may have lingered within you from your childhood. It's okay to admit that there are parts of your past that still sting. Take a moment to breathe, and allow yourself to recognize those moments or experiences that have left a mark on your heart. Write them down. Remember, it's not about dwelling on the pain but about bravely acknowledging it so we can start the healing process.

_____

_____

_____

_____

_____

Step 2: Get Curious

Now, let's ignite that curious spirit within you. Ask yourself why those memories or experiences still affect you today. Write down what emotions arise when you think about them. Be patient and compassionate with yourself as you explore these feelings. Getting curious is not about self-blame but about understanding the connections between your past and your present. It's like peeling back the layers of an onion, one by one, to reveal your inner truth.

_____

_____

_____

_____

_____

Step 3: Connect the Dots

The last step is about connecting the dots. See if you can identify patterns or themes that emerge from your exploration. Write down if there are recurring situations, behaviors, or emotions that seem to have their roots in your past. This is where the puzzle pieces of your inner child's story start coming together. Connecting the dots isn't about casting blame but about gaining insight and understanding into the ways your past has shaped your present.

_____

_____

_____

_____

_____

_____

_____

Remember, this process is about self-compassion, self-discovery, and self-growth. By acknowledging what hurts, getting curious, and connecting the dots, you're taking the first brave steps toward healing your wounded inner child.

Beyond the Obvious Trauma

We're diving deep, looking beyond the obvious, and exploring the subtle, often overlooked forms of trauma that may have left their mark on your inner child. These hidden wounds can manifest in various ways and impact your emotional well-being in ways you might not even realize. It's crucial to acknowledge and address these traumas in order to truly heal.

Let's take a moment to consider some of these subtle forms of trauma:

- **Dealing with narcissism:** If you grew up with a narcissistic parent or caregiver, you may have experienced emotional neglect and manipulation that left lasting scars.
- **Emotional invalidation:** Sometimes, our feelings and experiences are dismissed or belittled, making us feel unheard and invalidated. This can be a form of emotional trauma that affects our self-esteem.
- **The family scapegoat:** If you were the family scapegoat, you may have endured constant blame and criticism, leading to a profound sense of unworthiness.
- **Cultural and religious trauma:** Cultural and religious beliefs can shape our upbringing and sometimes lead to inner conflicts, guilt, or confusion that require healing.
- **Emotional void in affluence:** Growing up in an affluent family doesn't guarantee emotional fulfillment. Sometimes, material wealth can mask emotional neglect.
- **Parentification:** Being forced to take on adult responsibilities as a child can be a form of trauma, robbing you of your childhood.
- **Generational trauma:** Trauma can be passed down through generations, affecting your sense of self and emotional well-being.
- **Attachment disruptions:** Insecure or disrupted attachments during childhood can leave you struggling with trust and intimacy in adulthood.
- **Microaggressions and marginalization:** Experiencing subtle acts of discrimination or bias can accumulate over time, impacting your self-worth and self-identity.

- **Educational trauma:** Negative experiences in school, such as bullying or academic pressure, can shape your beliefs about your abilities and potential.

Now, you might be wondering, "Why should I explore all these painful aspects of my past?" The answer is simple: acknowledging these experiences is a huge step in healing. While it may be tough to confront these wounds, it's a necessary part of your journey to a healthier relationship with yourself and others, improved emotional regulation, and a stronger sense of self.

MYTHS ABOUT TRAUMA

I want to debunk some common myths and misconceptions about trauma that may have been weighing heavily on your heart. It's important to address these misunderstandings with compassion and clarity so you can embark on your inner child healing journey with a sense of hope and confidence.

Myth: Trauma survivors are permanently broken.

- You might feel like your brain has suddenly changed who you are because of the adaptations it developed to cope with trauma. However, none of these changes are irreversible. Just as your brain learned these adaptations, it can unlearn them. Healing is possible, and you can reclaim your true self.

Myth: Only combat soldiers get PTSD.

- PTSD is not limited to combat soldiers. It's a normal reaction to traumatic events that can affect anyone, regardless of their background. Trauma has been a part of human and animal experience throughout history. It's essential to recognize that your experience is valid, no matter the source of trauma.

Myth: Not talking about it will help me get over it.

- It's a tempting belief that avoiding discussing your trauma will make it disappear. Sadly, this isn't true. Your body and brain will remember the trauma, whether or not you talk about it. The impact of trauma can persist even if it remains unspoken. Healing often involves acknowledging and processing these experiences.

Myth: Time heals all wounds.

- While time can aid in the healing of some wounds, trauma is unique. Unaddressed trauma wounds have a tendency to fester. Just as physical injuries may require specific interventions such as stitches or surgery, psychological injuries may also require attention to facilitate healing.

Myth: I'll never be "normal."

- What does the concept of "normal" truly entail? When you question whether you will ever achieve a sense of "normalcy" again, what you're truly seeking is a feeling of safety, the ability to live free from symptoms, and the opportunity to define your life beyond the impact of trauma. The resounding answer is YES! Although trauma may seem insurmountable, it is something that can be addressed. With the appropriate interventions, you can embark on a journey of healing and flourishing.

Myth: In order to heal, I'll have to forgive.

- You are not obligated to forgive anyone who has caused you harm in order to heal. Healing is a deeply personal journey, and forgiveness, if it happens, is just one aspect of it. Do not allow the expectation to forgive to discourage you from pursuing the healing you rightfully deserve. Your well-being is not contingent on forgiving those who have caused you pain.

These myths can be heavy burdens to carry, but with knowledge and the right guidance, you can overcome them.

I encourage you to take some time to reflect on which of the above myths you may have believed to be true. It can be helpful to write down how these misconceptions may have negatively impacted your approach to your own trauma.

_____

_____

_____

_____

_____

GENERATIONAL PATTERNS AND BELIEFS

Imagine for a moment the way cherished family traditions, precious heirlooms, the unique shade of your family's hair color, and those secret recipes passed down through generations hold a special place in your heart. In a similar way, trauma can also be passed down, often referred to as generational trauma, intergenerational trauma, or transgenerational trauma. It's like an invisible thread woven into the fabric of your family's history, touching not only you but also those who came before you.

Generational trauma often starts with a traumatic event that causes intense distress, affecting not just individuals but also economic, cultural, and family aspects of life. Future generations may unknowingly inherit this trauma, carrying the burden of their ancestors' pain. This inheritance can occur quietly, hidden within unspoken struggles, discrimination, and prejudice that continue within family dynamics.

Now, let's explore how generational trauma directly impacts your inner child—the precious part of you that we are working to heal together:

- **A lack of self-worth:** Generational trauma can chip away at your sense of self-worth, causing you to question your value and significance. These doubts often stem from the negative beliefs and self-criticism handed down through generations.
- **Anxiety:** The anxiety you grapple with may have roots in the collective anxiety of your ancestors. The unresolved fears and anxieties from past generations can seep into your very being, leading to anxiety without an apparent cause.
- **Depersonalization:** Feeling detached from yourself and your surroundings can be a way your inner child copes with generational trauma. It's a protective mechanism, shielding you from overwhelming emotions.
- **Depression:** Generational trauma can feel like a heavy burden you've inherited, leading to feelings of hopelessness and sadness that manifest as depression.
- **Emotional numbness:** Sometimes, generational trauma leaves you feeling emotionally numb, making it challenging to connect with your own feelings and those of others.
- **Impaired life skills:** Struggling with essential life skills like critical thinking, decision-making, or time management can be a consequence of generational trauma. These skills may not have been adequately nurtured due to the trauma's impact on your family.
- **PTSD symptoms:** For some, symptoms of PTSD may emerge as a result of generational trauma. This can

include feeling socially isolated, battling negative thoughts, or losing interest in once-beloved hobbies.

Moreover, recent research has shown that generational trauma may even impact our physical health (Merrick et al., 2019).

Understanding generational trauma is a pivotal milestone in your healing journey. It's the moment when you realize that the struggles you face are not yours alone to bear. By embracing this knowledge, you can start to break free from the cycle and lay the foundation for healing your precious inner child.

Understanding the Influence of Generational Patterns and Beliefs

Generational patterns and beliefs are like an invisible thread that runs through your family tree, passing down attitudes, behaviors, and emotional responses from one generation to the next. These patterns and beliefs are not always positive; they can also carry generational trauma, pain, and suffering.

The first step in healing generational patterns is to identify them. Ask yourself if there are any irrational fears or strong negative emotions associated with certain people, places, songs, or events in your life. These feelings can often be rooted in your family's history. You might wonder why a simple tune brings you to tears or why a specific location triggers intense anxiety. For example, a young women could never understand why the smell of whiskey immediately made her anxious and nervous. It would later be revealed that this was her stepfather's drink of choice. When he drank, he became physically abusive. This memory was buried and became generational trauma that she carried with her into her adult life. Write down anything that comes to mind below.

_____

_____

_____

_____

_____

_____

_____

_____

_____

_____

Questions for self-reflection:

- **Is it a learned behavior from my parents or a condition of my upbringing?** Take a moment to reflect on whether you've learned these reactions from your family or if they were ingrained in your childhood.
- **Did my parents or grandparents go through any traumatic experiences?** Sometimes, generational trauma is passed down through the family, impacting each successive generation.

Once you've explored these questions, you might uncover a profound truth: that some of your struggles are not entirely yours to bear. They may have been passed down to you. As an adult, you may not drink at all, so why would the smell of whiskey upset you so much? None of your friends drink, and your idea of a great night out is going to catch a move. But you were carrying generational trauma that wasn't yours to hold. This realization can be both liberating and empowering.

Shedding Shame and Responsibility

Understanding the origin of your pain, fear, or self-doubt can help you shed the burden of shame and misplaced responsibility. You can put these emotions back where they belong—with the past generations who initially carried them. Recognize that you are not to blame for the generational patterns, but you do have the power to break free from them.

Now that you've identified the influence of generational patterns and beliefs in your life, it's time to take action. Here's a practical exercise to help you get started:

Exercise: Breaking Free From Generational Patterns

- **Create a family tree:** Draw a family tree that includes at least three generations. Note any significant traumas or recurring patterns you are aware of in your family's history.

CREATE A FAMILY TREE:

DRAW A FAMILY TREE THAT INCLUDES AT LEAST THREE GENERATIONS. NOTE ANY SIGNIFICANT TRAUMAS OR RECURRING PATTERNS YOU ARE AWARE OF IN YOUR FAMILY'S HISTORY.

Mom's Family Tree

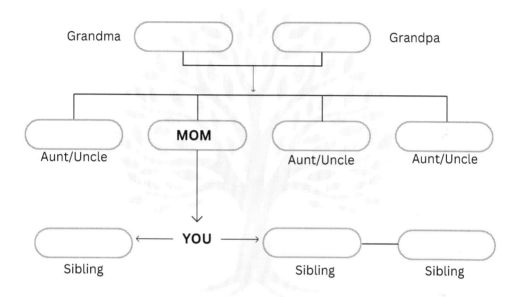

Grandma

Grandpa

Aunt/Uncle

MOM

Aunt/Uncle

Aunt/Uncle

Sibling

YOU

Sibling

Sibling

List any family recurring patterns or significant traumas.

DRAW A FAMILY TREE THAT INCLUDES AT LEAST THREE
GENERATIONS. NOTE ANY SIGNIFICANT TRAUMAS OR RECURRING
PATTERNS YOU ARE AWARE OF IN YOUR FAMILY'S HISTORY.

Dad's Family Tree

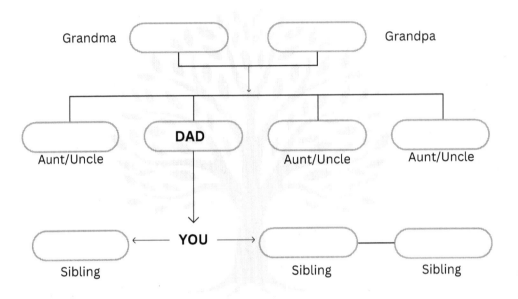

Grandma

Grandpa

Aunt/Uncle

DAD

Aunt/Uncle

Aunt/Uncle

Sibling

YOU

Sibling

Sibling

List any family recurring patterns or significant traumas.

Write a letter: Write a heartfelt letter to your ancestors, expressing your understanding of the generational patterns and your intention to break free from them. This can be a powerful way to release pent-up emotions and gain closure.

_____

_____

_____

_____

_____

_____

_____

_____

_____

_____

Breaking free from generational patterns and beliefs is a courageous step toward healing your wounded inner child. Remember, you have the strength and resilience to overcome these inherited challenges. Embrace this empowering journey, and with each step, you'll find yourself developing a healthier relationship with yourself and others, improving your emotional regulation, and strengthening your sense of self.

Family Dynamics and Inherited Emotional Responses

Let's begin by acknowledging that certain emotional processes are deeply rooted in your environment and the situations you've encountered throughout your life. Some of these you may have learned over time, and they've become a part of you, shaping your reactions and beliefs for years to come.

However, there's another layer to this emotional tapestry—inherited emotional responses. This is where the concept of mirror neurons comes into play, and it's a powerful tool for understanding how your "genetics" can influence your emotions.

Mirror neurons are incredible brain cells that act in the same way when you perform an action as when you observe someone else doing it. Imagine this: If you watched your mother yell and scream every time your father came home late, you might have noticed that you, too, experience a similar emotional response when your spouse is late. It's as if the neurons in your brain are firing in perfect harmony.

So, what does this mean for your emotional processes? Well, these mirror neurons create an "emotional resemblance" between you and your family members. It's only natural that you would pick up on certain behaviors and traits when you've lived with specific people for years. Your parents, for instance, likely raised you based on the things they experienced during their own childhood, including the emotions they felt. They passed on values and beliefs that you unconsciously absorbed, without DNA being the sole factor.

The fascinating part about mirror neurons and emotional inheritance is that you might share emotional traits with your ancestors simply because of certain behaviors and traits that have been passed down through generations.

Why Is It Important?

It's essential to recognize that not all emotions, behaviors, or traits are positive. Some may have been learned through years of experiences and hardships that have left a mark on your family's history. This is where your active engagement in healing and personal growth comes into play.

It can be challenging to confront and change emotional processes that have been ingrained in your family for generations. It might feel like you're plucking a piece of your own identity or your family history out of your mind. But remember, change is possible and necessary.

Don't let this realization overwhelm you. You have the power to break unhealthy cycles and make positive changes. In fact, it's vital, especially if you have children, to ensure that certain emotional processes are not passed down to the next generation.

Interactive Mind Mapping Exercise

This exercise will enable you to visually organize and understand the various aspects of your personal history. By doing so, you'll gain valuable insights into your inner child's needs and begin the process of healing and reparenting.

Gather Your Materials

Find a quiet, comfortable space where you can be peaceful and focus on your tasks without any distractions.

Set Your Intention

Take a moment to set your intention for this exercise. Remind yourself that you are engaging in this process to heal, nurture, and support your inner child.

_____

_____

_____

Start With Your Core Beliefs

In the center of your paper, write down a core belief about yourself that you would like to explore or change. For example, you might write, "I am hard to love" or "I am not good enough." This belief is at the heart of your inner child's wounds.

Connect to Childhood Experiences

Now, draw branches radiating outward from your core belief, like the spokes of a wheel. On each branch, write down specific memories or experiences from your childhood that contributed to this belief. These could be moments of neglect, criticism, or any other significant events that shaped your self-perception.

Family Patterns

Create additional branches stemming from the core belief and link them to your family members. Write down how each family member, including parents, siblings, and caregivers, played a role in reinforcing or instilling this belief. Consider their actions, words, and behaviors.

Emotional Responses

Extend your mind map by adding branches that detail the emotions you felt during these childhood experiences. Did you feel sadness, anger, fear, or shame? Write down these emotions connected to each memory or family pattern.

Challenging the Belief

As you continue to expand your mind map, create branches that represent moments in your life when you started to challenge or question this core belief. These may be instances of personal growth, therapy, or support from others. Write down the positive changes or shifts in perspective that occurred.

Self-Reflection

Take some time to reflect on your mind map. Notice any patterns, connections, or insights that emerge. Are there recurring themes in your childhood experiences or family dynamics? What emotions do you associate with certain memories? How have these beliefs affected your relationships and emotional well-being?

_____

_____

_____

_____

_____

_____

_____

Reparenting Intentions

Finally, make a commitment to yourself. Write down how you intend to reparent your wounded inner child in light of the insights gained from your mind map. What steps can you take to challenge and transform your core beliefs? How can you provide the love, care, and support that your inner child needs?

_____

_____

_____

_____

_____

_____

_____

Remember, this exercise is not a one-time event but a valuable tool for ongoing self-discovery and healing. You can revisit and update your mind map as you make progress in your inner child healing journey.

INNER CHILD JOURNAL PROMPTS

You will find these prompts at the end of each chapter. The goal is to encourage self-reflection and active engagement in the healing process. Let's begin:

- **Childhood superpowers:** Reflect on the unique qualities and strengths you had as a child. Write about how these qualities can be a source of resilience and healing for your inner child today.

_____

_____

_____

_____

_____

- **Creating a safe haven:** Describe in detail a safe and comforting place that your inner child can visit whenever they need solace. Include sensory details like sights, sounds, and smells to make it vivid and real.

_____

_____

_____

_____

_____

- **Rewriting childhood stories:** Think of a fairy tale or story from your childhood. Rewrite this story with a more empowering and healing narrative. How would this new version of the story impact your inner child's beliefs about themselves and the world?

_____

_____

_____

_____

_____

- **Emotional archeology:** Reflect on a specific childhood memory that still triggers strong emotions. Write down the details of the memory and explore why it continues to affect you. What unmet needs or desires from your inner child are tied to this memory?

_____

_____

_____

_____

_____

- **Inner child's wish list:** Imagine asking your inner child what they wish for in life. What are their desires, hopes, and dreams? How can you work toward fulfilling some of these wishes now?

_____

_____

_____

_____

_____

In this chapter, we've explored the depths of your inner world, uncovering childhood wounds, family dynamics, and the core beliefs that have shaped your self-perception. You've engaged in exercises designed to foster self-compassion and self-awareness.

In the next chapter, we will delve even deeper into the heart of CBT therapy for inner child healing. We'll focus on confronting and transforming the negative beliefs and behaviors that stem from these traumas. It's an essential step in breaking free from the cycle of pain and embracing a healthier, more empowered way of living.

Prepare yourself for some challenging but incredibly rewarding work ahead. You have the strength within you to rewrite the narratives that have been holding you back for far too long. It's time to break free from the chains of the past and step into a future where you are the author of your own story.

4

CHALLENGING NEGATIVE BELIEFS AND BEHAVIORS

The most potent muse of all is our own inner child.

— STEPHEN NACHMANOVITCH

This chapter is dedicated to equipping you with the tools and strategies you need to recognize and transform those negative patterns rooted in past traumas. It's time to empower yourself with the skills for lasting positive change.

You might be wondering: How can connecting with your inner child inspire you to challenge and transform negative beliefs and behaviors? It's an important question and one that we will explore deeply throughout this chapter.

Our inner child carries within it the memories and experiences of our past, both the beautiful and the painful. Sometimes, these beliefs and behaviors served as coping mechanisms when we were young, helping us survive difficult times. But as we grow, some of these patterns can become outdated and no longer serve us well.

By reconnecting with your inner child and understanding the origins of your beliefs and behaviors, you gain a profound insight into yourself. This awareness is the first step toward change. When you recognize these patterns for what they are—survival strategies from your past—you can begin to challenge and transform them into healthier, more adaptive ways of thinking and behaving.

As we progress through this chapter, you can expect to gain improved emotional regulation and a stronger sense of self. Most importantly, you will acquire valuable tools for ongoing personal growth and emotional resilience.

Let's get started on the path to challenging and transforming those negative beliefs and behaviors that no longer serve you. Together, I will help you become the empowered and resilient person you are meant to be.

RECOGNIZING AND ADDRESSING NEGATIVE THOUGHT PATTERNS

All-Or-Nothing Thinking

Do you tend to see things in black and white? Are you often caught in the trap of thinking that if something isn't perfect, it's a total failure? This is called "all or nothing" thinking. To overcome it, start noticing when you fall into this pattern. Challenge yourself to find shades of gray and appreciate the progress, no matter how small.

Over-Generalization

Over-generalization involves making sweeping conclusions based on a single event or a few instances. Are you guilty of saying things like, "I always mess up" or "Everyone lets me down"? Recognize when you're over-generalizing, and remember that one mistake or disappointment doesn't define your entire life.

Mental Filter

Do you have a mental filter that only allows negative thoughts to enter? It's like seeing the world through a gloomy lens. To combat this, catch yourself when you're filtering out the positive aspects of a situation. Challenge yourself to notice the silver linings and the good things happening around you.

Discounting the Positive

Some of us have a tendency to downplay our achievements or dismiss compliments as if they don't count. When you discount the positive, you're robbing yourself of well-deserved self-esteem boosts. Begin acknowledging your accomplishments and accept compliments graciously.

Jumping to Conclusions

Are you a mind reader, assuming you know what others are thinking about you? Or do you often predict the worst outcome without any evidence? Challenge these tendencies by seeking evidence and asking for clarification when needed.

Mind Reading

Similar to jumping to conclusions, mind reading involves believing you can predict what others think about you. Remember that you cannot read minds, and it's okay to ask for feedback and communicate openly with others.

Fortune Telling

Fortune telling is the art of predicting doom and gloom in the future. When you find yourself thinking, "This will never work out," remind yourself that the future is uncertain, and you have the power to shape it through your actions and choices.

Magnifying and Minimization

Do you magnify your mistakes and minimize your successes? Challenge these tendencies by giving equal weight to your achievements and acknowledging your worth.

Perfectionism

Striving for greatness is commendable, but being a perfectionist can be crippling. Allow yourself to embrace imperfection as a natural part of growth and learning.

Self-Blame and Self-Putdown

Lastly, self-blame and self-putdowns are destructive thought patterns that can keep you trapped in a cycle of self-criticism. Remember to practice self-compassion and acknowledge that making mistakes is a part of being human.

Recognizing these negative thought patterns is a significant step to healing your wounded inner child. Each time you catch yourself in one of these patterns, replace it with a more balanced, compassionate thought.

Remember, you are strong, capable, and deserving of love and healing.

How to Challenge and Reframe

We know that CBT is a powerful tool that can help you regain control over your thoughts and emotions. The concept is rooted in the interconnectedness of our thoughts, feelings, and behaviors. By identifying and changing negative thought patterns, we can create a positive ripple effect throughout our lives.

Practical Exercises to Challenge and Reframe Negative Thoughts

- **Progressive muscle relaxation:** A relaxation technique that involves tensing and then relaxing each muscle group in the body, one at a time. By consciously releasing tension from your muscles, you can also release mental stress and anxiety. As you go through the process, visualize the tension leaving your body, making way for a sense of calm and tranquility to take its place. This practice can help you achieve a state of deep relaxation and promote overall well-being.

- **Relaxed breathing:** When you're feeling overwhelmed by negative thoughts, practice relaxed breathing. Slow, deep breaths can calm your nervous system and help you think more clearly.

- **Cognitive reframing:** This is where CBT really shines. When a negative thought pops up, pause and ask yourself if it's based on facts or assumptions. Challenge the thought by seeking evidence that supports or contradicts it. For instance, if you think, "I'm always a failure," ask yourself, "What are some examples where I've succeeded or improved?"

- **ABC functional analysis:** ABC stands for Activating Event, Beliefs, and Consequences. When a negative thought occurs, identify the event that triggered it, the belief you hold about yourself or the situation, and the emotional and behavioral consequences. This exercise helps you dissect and understand the thought pattern. For example, imagine you're at work, and your boss asks to speak with you in private. This would be the action that triggered your emotional event. Next, identify the belief you hold about yourself or the situation. "I must be in trouble. I am going to get fired. I did poorly on an assignment." These beliefs are based on assumptions and self-worth. These are the negative thought patterns you need to address. Now, let's analyze the consequences of these beliefs. You may feel anxious or stressed. When you meet with your boss, you may have trouble making eye contact or appear fidgety. This ABC Functional Analysis helps you break down the situation into its components, allowing you to see how your beliefs about the event are directly linked to your emotional and behavioral reactions. The power of this exercise lies in recognizing that your beliefs may not always be accurate or helpful.

- **Thought record:** Keep a thought journal to track and analyze negative thoughts. Write down the thought, the emotions it triggers, and the evidence for and against it. This process can help you identify recurring patterns and challenge them effectively.

The Tough Love Approach

Now, I want to remind you of something crucial. Challenging negative thought patterns can be tough, especially when they've been ingrained for years. But remember, the path to healing often involves discomfort and facing the past. It's like retraining a muscle that has been neglected—it may hurt initially, but with consistent effort, it grows stronger.

You are strong enough to do this. You are worthy of healing.

With each thought you challenge and reframe, you're breaking free from the chains of your past and paving the way for a brighter, more fulfilling future. Keep moving forward, and don't hesitate to reach out if you need support.

BEHAVIOR MODIFICATION STRATEGIES

You might be thinking, "Can I really change my behaviors?" The answer is a resounding yes! The journey toward healing your wounded inner child involves not just understanding the past but actively engaging in the present to create a brighter future.

Let's start by discussing the stages of behavior change. These stages will be your roadmap as you work toward becoming the best version of yourself.

- **Precontemplation:** This is the stage where you might not even realize that a particular behavior needs to change. It's essential to acknowledge that you may have behaviors stemming from your wounded inner child. Start by becoming aware of these behaviors without judgment. Ask yourself, "What aspects of my behavior might be related to my past experiences?"
- **Contemplation:** In this stage, you recognize that a behavior is problematic and needs to change. You're contemplating the idea of making a change but haven't taken any concrete steps yet. This is a pivotal moment where you're acknowledging the need for healing. Be

gentle with yourself during this stage and explore the reasons behind your behaviors.

- **Preparation:** You're getting ready to make a change. You've decided to work on healing your inner child, and you're taking steps to prepare yourself for action. This might involve research, seeking support, or setting goals. It's crucial to be patient and give yourself the time needed to prepare.

- **Action:** This is where the rubber meets the road. You're actively making changes in your behavior. It might involve using the tools and techniques you've learned, practicing self-compassion, and consciously choosing healthier behaviors. Remember, change takes effort and persistence, but you're capable of it!

- **Maintenance:** Once you've made positive changes, it's important to maintain them. This stage is about reinforcing your new behaviors and making them a part of your daily life. You'll likely face challenges along the way, but with determination and support, you can stay on track.

- **Relapse:** It's normal to have setbacks. Don't be discouraged if you slip into old behaviors occasionally. Relapse is a natural part of the process. The key is to acknowledge it, learn from it, and get back on the path to healing. Be kind to yourself, and remember that progress is not always linear.

So, how do we alter harmful behaviors?

- **Identify cues:** The first step in behavior modification is recognizing the triggers or cues that lead to your harmful behaviors. Take some time to reflect on when and why you engage in these behaviors. Write down what emotions, situations, or people trigger them. Understanding your triggers is crucial to making positive changes.

_____

_____

_____

_____

_____

- **Disrupt the pattern:** Once you've identified your cues, it's time to disrupt the automatic pattern. When you feel the urge to engage in a harmful behavior, pause and take a deep breath. Create a brief mental or physical interruption to break the cycle. It can be as simple as counting to ten, taking a walk, or repeating a positive affirmation.
- **Replace with healthy alternatives:** Harmful behaviors often serve as coping mechanisms. To modify them successfully, you need to replace them with healthier alternatives. For example, if emotional eating is a problem, try substituting it with deep breathing exercises or a quick meditation session to manage stress or emotions.
- **Keep it simple:** Don't overwhelm yourself with trying to change too many behaviors all at once. Focus on one

or two harmful behaviors at a time. Once you've successfully modified them, move on to the next ones. Small, gradual changes are more sustainable and less daunting.

- **Think long term:** Healing your inner child and modifying behaviors is a huge journey. Be patient and kind to yourself. Instead of seeking instant results, focus on long-term improvement. Remind yourself of your ultimate goal—a healthier and happier you.

- **Persist:** There will be setbacks along the way, and that's perfectly normal. Don't let a slip-up discourage you. Keep persisting, and if you stumble, take the time you need to rest and return. Remember, change is rarely linear, and each step forward is a victory.

CASE STUDIES

Story One: The Belief of Not Enough

Hey there, I'm Tom, and I want to share with you a story about a belief that used to haunt me for years—the belief that I just wasn't enough. I felt inadequate in intelligence, height, appearance, talent, dedication, strength, and perseverance. It seemed like no matter what "it" was, I always fell short.

One of the toughest things about these limiting beliefs is how they fuel confirmation bias. When we hold onto a belief, we tend to actively search for evidence that supports it while brushing aside anything that contradicts it. It's just the way our minds work, but when it comes to limiting beliefs, it becomes a toxic loop.

As I desperately sought out proof to confirm my "not enough" belief, I unintentionally made it stronger. The more I reinforced this belief, the more success eluded me because I was constantly fixated on my perceived inadequacies. This self-fulfilling prophecy left me feeling empty and unsatisfied.

Limiting beliefs often take root during our childhood. They can be the result of messages from our parents or, like in my case, we create them ourselves as we try to make sense of our experiences. In my situation, I was a small and shy kid, making sports and making friends a real challenge. I jumped to the conclusion that I wasn't enough because these things were hard for me. Once that belief settled in, it was a tough one to break free from, thanks to the relentless confirmation bias.

Now, you might be curious about how I managed to break the shackles of "I'm not enough." Let me share with you the two strategies that made all the difference:

- **Mirror affirmations:** Mirror affirmations became my secret weapon in changing the way I talk to myself. By looking into the mirror and speaking kind, supportive words to myself, I learned to treat myself like a friend. This self-compassion and self-support played a crucial role in replacing those limiting beliefs with healthier ones.
- **Challenging beliefs with evidence:** I adopted a simple yet powerful habit– questioning myself with the words,

"How do I know?" Most of the time, when I held onto a belief rooted in my limiting beliefs, there was little to no real evidence to back it up. It was just a story I'd crafted. By consistently challenging these beliefs with evidence, I gradually weakened their grip on me.

This takes time, patience, and a heap of self-compassion. But trust me, these methods worked for me, and they can work for you too. As you journey through this workbook, you'll come across exercises and self-reflection activities that will guide you in applying these principles to your own life.

Here are three questions for you to ponder:

- **Exploring childhood roots:** Have you ever identified limiting beliefs or feelings of not being "enough" in your own life? Can you trace back to your childhood and pinpoint any experiences or messages that may have contributed to the formation of these beliefs? How might understanding their origins impact your journey of inner child healing?

- **Mirror affirmations and self-compassion:** Tom used mirror affirmations as a powerful tool to change his self talk and develop self-compassion. Have you ever tried mirror affirmations or similar self-compassion exercises? If so, what impact did they have on your self-perception and inner child healing? If not, how might incorporating self-compassion practices benefit your journey?

_____

_____

_____

_____

_____

- **Challenging beliefs with evidence:** Tom adopted the practice of challenging his limiting beliefs by asking, "How do I know?" This habit helped him weaken the grip of those beliefs. Can you identify any specific limiting beliefs you hold about yourself? How might consistently questioning and challenging these beliefs with evidence help you reframe them and foster a more positive self-image?

_____

_____

_____

_____

_____

Story Two: Waiting for the Shoe to Drop

I'm Chloe, and I want to take you on a personal journey through my experiences in inner child healing using CBT. My story is a testament to the fact that no matter how deeply rooted our negative beliefs and behaviors are; we have the power to challenge and change them.

My story begins in a challenging family environment where criticism was a daily occurrence. Growing up, I faced relentless scrutiny, even for the smallest imperfections. My childhood was marked by a constant pursuit of perfection and a pervasive fear that something would always go wrong. This upbringing left me with a habitual pattern of downplaying the positives in my life and constantly jumping to negative conclusions.

As an adult, I carried this heavy burden with me. I found it impossible to accept compliments gracefully because they always came with strings attached in my childhood. I lived in a state of constant anticipation of the worst possible outcome, even when everything seemed to be going perfectly. My mind was quick to think, "Something has to go wrong."

Eventually, I reached a breaking point. I realized that these negative thought patterns were robbing me of the joy and peace I deserved in my life. That's when I made the decision to embark on my journey of CBT therapy and healing my inner child.

I knew that challenging deeply ingrained thought patterns wouldn't be easy, but I was determined to break free from the chains of my past and retrain my brain. I made a commitment to this process, and here's how I began to transform my negative beliefs and behaviors:

- **Awareness:** I started by becoming acutely aware of my negative thoughts as they emerged. Recognizing when I was discounting the positives or jumping to conclusions was the first step.
- **Writing it down:** When a negative thought surfaced, I took a deep breath and physically wrote down what triggered it. I asked myself if it was a realistic thought or just a product of my past conditioning.
- **Challenging thoughts:** The hard work began as I challenged these thoughts. I questioned whether my fears were based on reality or merely echoes from my past. I practiced replacing these negative thoughts with more rational and positive ones.
- **Accepting compliments:** A significant breakthrough came when I learned to accept compliments with a simple "Thank you" instead of immediately dismissing them. Over time, I began to feel worthy of them and the value they added to my life.

I must admit that healing from the wounds of my childhood is an ongoing process. It requires daily commitment and effort to reshape my thinking patterns. However, the positive changes I experience every day keep me motivated. I am gradually rediscovering warmth, self-worth, and optimism that I had longed for.

Here are three reflective questions for you to ponder:

- **Self-reflective inquiry:** Are there any recurring negative thought patterns or beliefs from your own childhood that continue to influence your adult life? How might these patterns impact your current perceptions and behaviors, and what are the consequences of holding onto them?

———————————————————————

———————————————————————

———————————————————————

———————————————————————

———————————————————————

- **Awareness and mindfulness:** Have you ever consciously practiced being aware of your thoughts as they arise, similar to Chloe's process of recognizing negative thoughts? What insights have you gained from such awareness, and how might it relate to your own inner child healing journey?

———————————————————————

———————————————————————

———————————————————————

———————————————————————

———————————————————————

- **Transformation and growth:** Reflect on Chloe's journey of challenging and transforming her deeply ingrained thought patterns. What steps or strategies resonate with you in your own pursuit of inner child healing and personal growth? How might you apply these insights to begin reshaping your own thinking patterns for a more positive and fulfilling life?

_____

_____

_____

_____

_____

Story Three: She's So Mature for Her Age

I'm Joyce, and I want to share my journey with you—a journey filled with resilience and healing, where I unearthed the profound essence of love and compassion through the transformative practices of inner child work and CBT therapy.

My story began with a façade that garnered admiration from many. From a young age, I appeared mature, polite, and responsible to the outside world. But beneath that seemingly composed exterior, a painful truth lurked. My early life was marred by trauma inflicted by my alcoholic father. This trauma thrust me into adulthood far sooner than any child should experience, leaving me with a profound sense of being unloved and unwanted. I missed out on the innocence of childhood.

In my own words, I reflect on this painful ordeal: "The trauma I experienced matured me because I was never taught what love was or given any normal life lessons. I had to mature quickly because I was in survival mode. I had to learn how to survive in a house that was toxic and dysfunctional."

Many people praised me for my maturity, often remarking on how I seemed much older than my years. However, experts would later tell me that this can be a misleading response to childhood trauma. Children like me, who have faced such adversity, learn to adapt swiftly, to evade threats, and to make themselves as useful as possible. Unfortunately, this adaptive behavior can be mistaken for genuine maturity when, in truth, it's a survival mechanism.

As I transitioned into adulthood, I found myself ensnared in a cycle of meaningless relationships, haunted by an over-whelming fear of commitment. I had never truly grasped the art of love—neither for myself nor for others. My constant companions were self-doubt and self-criticism.

However, my story took a profound turn when tragedy struck. I lost my sister to cancer, and amidst my grief, I was confronted with an unexpected responsibility—raising my sister's five-year-old son, a young boy who had no one else. In that poignant moment, I realized that I needed to change, not only for my sake but for the well-being of my nephew.

My sister had committed herself to intensive therapy, prac-ticed CBT, and tirelessly worked on her inner child to provide her son with the best possible life. To honor my sister's memory, I resolved to follow the same path. I recognized the transformative power of inner child healing, and I embarked on a journey of self-discovery and healing with unwavering determination.

Here are three reflective questions for you to ponder:

- Have you ever felt the need to put on a facade to cope with challenging circumstances in your childhood? How did this affect your sense of self and your ability to experience the innocence of childhood?

_____

_____

_____

_____

_____

- Can you identify any patterns in your adult life that may be linked to unresolved childhood trauma or the need to adapt to difficult situations at a young age? How have these patterns impacted your relationships and emotional well-being?

_____

_____

_____

_____

_____

- Consider a moment in your life when you faced a significant personal challenge or tragedy. Did this experience lead to any profound realizations about yourself or the need for personal growth and healing?

_____

_____

_____

_____

_____

INNER CHILD JOURNAL PROMPTS

You will find these prompts at the end of each chapter. The goal is to encourage self-reflection and active engagement in the healing process. Let's begin:

- **Nurturing your inner child daily:** List three practical actions you can take every day to nurture and care for your inner child. These could be self-care routines, affirmations, or activities that bring you joy and comfort.

1. _____
2. _____
3. _____

- **Embracing vulnerability:** Reflect on a time when you felt vulnerable as a child and how it affected you. How can you embrace vulnerability in your adult life as a source of strength and connection rather than weakness?

_____

_____

_____

_____

_____

- **Healing through creativity:** Choose a creative outlet, such as drawing, painting, or crafting. Create an artwork that represents your inner child's journey toward healing. What colors, shapes, and symbols come to mind? What emotions does your creation evoke, and what insights does it provide about your inner child's needs?

_____

_____

_____

_____

_____

- **Parallel lives journaling:** Write a journal entry from the perspective of your inner child, describing a pivotal moment or significant event from your past. Then, write a follow-up entry from your current adult perspective, offering understanding, empathy, and guidance. How do these dual perspectives provide insights into your healing journey?

_____

_____

_____

_____

_____

- **Exploring forgotten memories:** Delve into your memory archives and try to recall a vivid, positive childhood memory that you haven't thought about in years. Describe it in detail, focusing on sensory experiences and emotions. How can you draw strength and inspiration from this forgotten moment in your inner child healing process?

_____

_____

_____

_____

_____

In this chapter, we've explored how CBT equips us with the tools to challenge and reframe our negative beliefs and behaviors. We've witnessed the transformative power of self-awareness and rational examination in overcoming self-defeating patterns. As we move forward into the next chapter, we will shift our focus toward building positive coping mechanisms. Armed with the skills acquired in this chapter, we will embark on a journey of self-empowerment, aiming to replace old habits with healthier and more adaptive strategies.

THE IMPORTANCE OF REFLECTION AND CELEBRATION

You have come so far on this journey of healing and self-discovery. Please take a moment to acknowledge the courage and strength it has taken to delve into your past, confront your inner child, and embrace the CBT techniques that are guiding you toward a brighter future. Every step you have taken is a testament to your resilience and commitment to healing.

As you pause here, breathe deeply and reflect on your progress. Remember the challenges you have faced and the emotional breakthroughs you have experienced. Celebrate your growth and the steps you have taken to reclaim your joy and emotional resilience.

I am incredibly proud of you. It takes immense bravery to embark on this journey, and your dedication is truly inspiring. As your healing journey progresses, you'll find a sense of peace and fulfillment that may have previously eluded you, and you'll recognize how many others could benefit from inner child healing.

I kindly ask you to share your experiences with this book by taking a few minutes of your time to share a brief review.

By leaving a review, you can help others who are on a similar path to discover these tools and techniques to heal their inner child and step forward into a brighter, more confident future.

Your insights and reflections can be a guiding light, offering support and encouragement to those who need it most.

Thank you for being a part of this transformative journey. Your voice matters, and together, we can create a ripple effect of healing and compassion.

Scan the QR Code to Leave Your Review

BUILDING POSITIVE COPING MECHANISMS

Honor your inner child by losing yourself in simple pleasures.

— KIM DEL VALLE WALKER

This is a pivotal step in your journey of inner child healing, where we'll explore practical strategies to empower you in dealing with life's challenges, stress, anxiety, and emotional turmoil. Think of this chapter as your treasure chest of tools for enhancing your emotional resilience.

As we delve into this chapter, I want you to remember that healing is an active process. It's about taking the reins of your emotional well-being and actively engaging with the strategies we'll explore here. You have already made incredible strides by acknowledging your wounded inner child, and now it's time to equip yourself with the skills to navigate life's ups and downs more effectively.

It's important to note that the real work lies in your active participation. Healing your inner child means taking charge of your own growth, and sometimes that requires pushing beyond your comfort zone.

The question I want you to ponder as you explore this chapter is: What simple joys could you reintroduce into your life to nurture and comfort your inner child? It's a question that calls for both self-reflection and action. The answers may surprise you, but they hold the key to unlocking a more resilient, joyful, and fulfilled version of yourself.

DEVELOPING HEALTHY COPING SKILLS

Developing healthy coping skills is a key aspect of your inner child healing journey. It's like giving yourself not just the toolbox but the matching toolbelt filled with powerful techniques to navigate life's challenges, both big and small. In this section, we're going to explore some CBT-based coping strategies that will be instrumental in helping you manage your emotional responses effectively. Let's dive right in:

Behavioral activation: Imagine your inner child as an active and playful spirit. Behavioral activation encourages you to reconnect with that inner child by engaging in activities that bring joy, satisfaction, and a sense of accomplishment. Start small, with activities you used to enjoy or new ones you're curious about. This strategy will help you rekindle your zest for life and boost your mood. For example, embrace your inner child's curiosity by exploring new places or activities. Visit a museum, go on a nature hike, or try a cooking class. New experiences can be invigorating for your spirit.

Problem-solving: Your inner child might feel overwhelmed by life's challenges. By breaking down problems into smaller, manageable chunks, you can empower yourself to take control. Identify the issue, brainstorm possible solutions, weigh the pros and cons, and take action. This process not only resolves the problem but also builds your self-confidence.

Exposure: Facing your fears or past traumas can be daunting but incredibly liberating. Exposure therapy gently encourages you to confront your anxieties one step at a time. Gradual exposure helps your inner child realize that they are safe and capable of handling difficult emotions and situations, fostering emotional resilience.

Guided discovery: This technique involves self-exploration and questioning to uncover negative thought patterns. You'll be amazed at how your inner child's beliefs have shaped your present behavior. Ask yourself questions like, "Why do I react this way?" and "What might my inner child be trying to protect me from?" This self-awareness is the key to understanding and healing.

Diaphragmatic breathing: Sometimes, our inner child needs a calming presence to soothe their fears. Diaphragmatic breathing is like a warm, comforting hug for your inner child. This technique involves taking deep breaths, filling your diaphragm with air, and exhaling slowly. It reduces stress and helps you stay grounded in the present moment.

Embrace these coping strategies with an open heart, and don't be discouraged if progress seems slow at times. Healing takes time, effort, and patience, but the rewards are worth it.

MINDFULNESS AND RELAXATION TECHNIQUES

Mindfulness is being fully present, observing your thoughts, emotions, and sensations without judgment, and cultivating a sense of self-compassion and awareness in the process. It's about tuning in to your inner world with an open heart and a curious mind.

A study showed that practicing mindfulness for just 15 minutes a day over 7 consecutive days improved emotion processing, including emotion intensity, emotional memory, and emotional attention bias. The study proved that this is an effective, convenient, safe, and standardized way to enhance emotion processing and maintain focus and peace (Wu et al., 2019).

So, how can the principles of mindfulness be helpful for emotional regulation on your journey to healing your wounded inner child?

Mindfulness is a practice that involves paying attention to the present moment with intention and without judgment. In the context of your inner child work, mindfulness becomes an essential companion, helping you connect with your emotions, thoughts, and sensations as they arise. Here's why it's so valuable:

Awareness of the present moment: Mindfulness encourages you to be fully present in the here and now. It's about letting go of dwelling on the past or worrying about the future and focusing on what's happening right at this very moment.

Non-judgmental observation: It's important to observe your inner child's wounds, emotions, and thought patterns without judgment. Mindfulness teaches you to accept whatever arises within you without labeling it as good or bad, right or wrong. This non-judgmental stance creates a safe space for your inner child to express themselves.

Emotional regulation: One of the primary benefits of mindfulness is its ability to help you regulate your emotions. By being present and non-judgmental, you can better understand your emotional triggers and responses. This awareness empowers you to choose how you respond to difficult emotions rather than reacting impulsively.

Self-compassion: Mindfulness also encourages self-compassion. When you treat your inner child's pain and struggles with kindness and understanding, you're fostering a sense of safety and trust within yourself. This nurturing attitude is vital for healing.

Reducing stress and anxiety: Inner child healing can sometimes bring up intense emotions and memories. Mindfulness techniques, such as deep breathing and meditation, can help reduce stress and anxiety, providing you with a calm and stable foundation for your healing journey.

Let's explore some mindfulness activities that will help you on your journey to healing your wounded inner child. These exercises will not only provide you with a sense of calm but will also empower you to explore your inner world and foster self-compassion. Remember, this process can be challenging, but it's all about nurturing yourself and making positive changes.

Body Deep Relaxation:

- Find a peaceful, cozy space where you can be undisturbed.
- Close your eyes and breathe deeply a few times to calm yourself.
- Begin at your toes, slowly tighten, and then relax each group of muscles in your body, working your way up.
- Be mindful of the sensations as you relax each muscle. Imagine releasing any emotional tension as you do so.

Mindfulness for Painful Feelings:

- When you're feeling overwhelmed by difficult emotions, take a moment to pause.
- Acknowledge the feeling without judgment. You might say, "I see you, sadness," or "I feel you, anger."
- Focus on your breath and allow yourself to fully experience the emotion without trying to change it.
- Remember that feelings are temporary, like passing clouds. They will eventually pass.

Mindfulness for Acknowledging Suffering:

- In times of emotional pain, sit quietly and reflect on the suffering you've experienced in the past.
- Validate your own pain and acknowledge that it's real, even if it's from your childhood.
- Allow yourself to grieve for the pain you endured as a child and the impact it has on your adult life.

Meditation on the Child:

- Imagine yourself at the age of five by closing your eyes.
- Picture your five-year-old self in a safe and loving environment.
- Send love and comfort to that child within you. You can say, "I love you, little [Your Name]. You are safe now."
- Allow yourself to feel the connection between your present self and your inner child.

Metta (Kindness) Meditation:

- Sit comfortably and bring to mind someone you care about deeply.
- Send them loving-kindness by saying, "May happiness be with you. May you enjoy good health. May you live with ease.
- Now, turn that loving-kindness inward and say the same words to yourself. "May I be happy. May I be healthy. May I live with ease."

- Extend this practice to include your inner child, wishing them well and healing.

Removing Objects Mindfulness:

- Select an object from your environment, something simple like a pebble or a leaf.
- Hold the object in your hand and observe it closely, paying attention to its texture, color, and shape.
- Allow your mind to focus solely on the object, letting go of any distracting thoughts.
- This exercise helps you practice present-moment awareness, which can be calming and grounding.

Remember, inner child healing is a journey that requires patience and persistence. These mindfulness activities are tools to help you navigate the process. Be gentle with yourself, and don't rush.

HOW TO INCORPORATE MINDFULNESS INTO DAILY LIFE

Let's delve into some practical tips on how to incorporate mindfulness into your daily life. Mindfulness is a powerful tool that can help you connect with your inner self, become more aware of your thoughts and feelings, and ultimately foster a healthier relationship with yourself and others.

- **Start with the basics:** Begin your day with a mindful ritual. It can be as simple as taking a few deep breaths and setting an intention for the day. This can help you ground yourself and set a positive tone for the hours ahead.

- **Mindful breathing:** Throughout the day, take a moment to pause and focus on your breath. Close your eyes if you can, and take a few slow, deep breaths. Pay attention to the sensation of the breath entering and leaving your body. This can help you stay present and calm, especially during challenging moments.

- **Mindful eating:** When you sit down to eat, truly savor each bite. Pay attention to the colors, textures, and flavors of your food. Eating mindfully can help you appreciate the nourishment you're providing to your body and enhance your connection to your physical sensations.

- **Body scan:** Dedicate a few minutes each day to a body scan. Start from the top of your head and slowly move your awareness down through your body, noticing any tension or discomfort. This practice can help you become more attuned to physical sensations and release stored tension.

- **Mindful journaling:** Set aside some time for reflective journaling. Write down your thoughts, feelings, and any insights that come to you during the day. This practice can help you process your emotions and gain a deeper understanding of your inner world.

ESTABLISHING A SELF-CARE ROUTINE

Self-care is not just about pampering yourself with bubble baths or spa days but about nurturing your wounded inner child in a holistic way. Together, we'll explore the six elements of self-care specific to adults with childhood trauma and understand why they are essential for your mental and emotional well-being.

The Importance of Self-Care in Healing and Mental Health

Before we dive into the elements of self-care tailored to your unique needs, let's first emphasize the overarching importance of self-care in your healing journey. Healing from childhood trauma is a profound and courageous undertaking. It requires patience, self-compassion, and a commitment to your own well-being. Here's why self-care is non-negotiable:

- **Self-care is self-respect:** By prioritizing self-care, you're acknowledging your worthiness of love and care, just as you would care for a loved one. Remember, you are your own greatest advocate.
- **Stress reduction:** Childhood trauma often leaves us with heightened stress levels. Regular self-care practices help to reduce stress, promoting better mental and physical health.
- **Emotional regulation:** A self-care routine helps you manage intense emotions that may arise during your healing process. It equips you with tools to navigate these feelings with grace and understanding.

- **Healing and growth:** Healing is an active process. Self-care provides you with the nurturing environment needed for your inner child to heal and grow. It creates the fertile soil for transformation.

Now, let's explore the six elements of self-care tailored to adults with childhood trauma. These elements will serve as building blocks for your personalized self-care routine:

Bad Parents, Bad Me

This element centers around challenging and reframing negative self-beliefs that may have stemmed from childhood experiences. We are born to learn and grow, needing more than just the basics to thrive. It's crucial for our well-being that someone loves and recognizes us for who we are. Feeling stable and okay inside is really important.

We can struggle to understand our feelings and keep things in order if we didn't learn to take care of ourselves when we were younger; it can make us feel confused and like something's missing in how we see ourselves. We can make assumptions that if our parents were toxic, dysfunctional, or "bad," then as a reflection, so are we.

Even if we have support and inner strength, tough times in our past can make life harder. It's like mirrors sometimes make us see ourselves in a way that's not true.

Gifted Children

We have a unique ability to survive tough situations by blocking off certain parts of ourselves. It's like a ship sealing off compartments when it has a hole to stay afloat, especially when we're young and still figuring out how to handle our emotions and make decisions. We do this because we rely on others for our basic needs and emotional support.

As we grow older, we may find these hidden parts of ourselves that we tucked away for later. What really matters is what we choose to do with these gifted parts. Some people may struggle to find a positive outcome, but others can change their story in a way that makes them feel more alive instead of shutting down.

Conflict Over Values

Examine your values and beliefs and ensure they align with your authentic self. Sometimes, trauma can lead to confusion or distortion of values. Self-care here involves realigning your values with your true essence.

Freud talked about three basic parts of the mind: the id, which is all about desires and drives, the superego, which is like the voice of our parents telling us what's right and wrong, and the ego, which develops like a protective layer and helps balance these two.

If our sense of self is strong, it means we've figured out how to handle and balance the conflicts between our inner desires and what society expects of us. We can pursue our goals in a balanced and independent way. But if there's too much conflict between our inner desires and society's rules, our passions might become overwhelming and obsessive.

Anger and Injury

Healing often involves processing and releasing anger and hurt. This self-care element guides you in acknowledging and safely expressing your emotions, allowing for deep emotional healing.

When we get hurt, we often jump straight to anger, especially when we feel we've been treated unfairly. We skip over feeling the actual hurt and vulnerability and react with defensive anger, which can make us seem threatening to others.

This reaction can backfire, especially when the other person didn't mean to hurt us or it was just a misunderstanding. In these cases, we push away the very person who could help us heal, and this can prevent our wounds from getting better.

Pride and Shame

Explore feelings of pride and shame that may have been instilled during your childhood. Self-care here involves building self-esteem and self-worth and recognizing your inherent value.

Having a healthy sense of pride is good. Good parents can be proud of their kids without making them feel like they have to do things to earn that love. They can also provide guidance, even when it's hard, without taking away the feeling of pride. When parents show they care, it helps us feel good about ourselves.

But too much pride can be a problem. It can make us think we're better than we actually are, and that can lead to big mistakes. If we're too stuck on feeling proud, we won't be able to learn from our mistakes. Underneath that kind of pride, there's often hidden shame.

Humor and Gratitude

Laughter and gratitude can be powerful tools in your healing journey. Cultivate a sense of humor and gratitude in your life, even in the face of adversity. This self-care element fosters positivity and resilience.

Humor can be tricky, especially when it's mean or sarcastic. While it can be a temporary way to cope, it can also hurt us in the long run. Being curious about ourselves and using gentle humor can be a way to make peace with ourselves. Sometimes, it's okay to get a little mad at ourselves and then laugh at how silly we can be. It doesn't always work when someone else finds humor in our mistakes, but sometimes it can help.

Remember, self-care is not a one-time event but a lifelong commitment to your well-being. By incorporating these six elements into your self-care routine, you're creating a solid foundation for inner child healing, improved emotional regulation, and a stronger sense of self.

Common Self-Care Misconceptions

Let's address some common misconceptions about self-care before we get into creating a personalized self-care routine.

Misconception 1: Self-Care Is Self-Indulgence

Self-care is often misunderstood as a luxury reserved for special occasions. The truth is that self-care is a necessity, not a luxury. It's not about being selfish; it's about recognizing your worth and taking steps to maintain your well-being.

Misconception 2: Self-Care Requires a Lot of Time and Money

You don't need to spend hours or loads of money on self-care. Effective self-care can be simple and budget-friendly. It's about finding what works for you and making it a regular part of your life.

Misconception 3: Self-Care Is Only About Physical Health

While physical self-care is important, it's only one piece of the puzzle. Emotional, mental, and spiritual self-care are equally vital. Self-care should address your overall well-being, not just the surface.

Creating a Self-Care Routine

Now, let's move on to creating a self-care routine that suits you and your inner child healing journey. Follow these step-by-step guidelines:

Step 1: Self-Reflection

Begin by reflecting on your unique needs. What activities or practices make you feel rejuvenated, calm, and centered? What has helped you cope with emotional challenges in the past? Make a list of these things.

1._____
2._____
3._____
4._____
5._____

Step 2: Prioritize Self-Care

Understand that self-care is not negotiable. It's a commitment to your well-being. Schedule regular self-care time in your calendar, just like you would for any other important task. Treat it with the same level of dedication.

Step 3: Start Small and Build Consistency

Begin with manageable self-care activities that fit into your daily routine. Whether it's a 10-minute meditation session, a brief journaling exercise, or a short walk in nature, consistency is key. Gradually add more self-care practices as you become comfortable.

Step 4: Tailor Self-Care to Your Needs

Remember that self-care is personal. What works for someone else may not work for you. Experiment with different activities and find what resonates with you. It might include reading, painting, cooking, or even simply resting.

Step 5: Self-Compassion and Boundaries

Practice self-compassion. Be kind to yourself, especially if you've struggled with self-care in the past. Set boundaries to protect your self-care time and communicate these boundaries with loved ones if necessary.

Step 6: Monitor and Adjust

Regularly assess the effectiveness of your self-care routine. Are you feeling better emotionally and mentally? Are you more resilient in the face of challenges? If not, make adjustments to your routine as needed.

Practical Self-Care Tips

Leave That Snooze Button Alone

Many people incorporate a bit of extra snooze time into their morning routine, thinking it's a kinder way to wake up. However, this can actually disrupt your sleep cycle, leaving you feeling groggier. Instead, consider setting your alarm for when you truly need to get up to ensure a more restful night's sleep.

Let the Sunlight In

Starting your day by opening the blinds can be a refreshing way to greet the morning. Just a few minutes of natural light can boost your vitamin D levels and help balance stress hormones like cortisol. It's a simple and beneficial ritual.

Embrace Indoor Greenery

Apart from keeping the air cleaner, having houseplants can also lift your spirits. Research suggests that interacting with indoor plants may calm your nervous system and reduce blood pressure, fostering an overall sense of tranquility (Lee et al., 2015). If you're not confident in your gardening skills, opt for low-maintenance plants like succulents or air plants.

Read Uplifting Stories Daily

In a world filled with stress-inducing news, it's essential to prioritize your mental well-being. Consider swapping out some of your daily news consumption for the joy of reading an uplifting book. It can be a small but significant act of self-care.

EXERCISE: 30-DAY SELF-CARE CALENDAR

Create your own 1-month calendar of self-care activities, challenging yourself to do at least one activity each day.

- **Get a calendar:** Start by grabbing a blank calendar for the upcoming month. Whether it's a physical calendar or a digital one, choose a format that works best for you.
- **Identify your self-care goals:** Take a moment to think about your inner child's needs. What kind of self-care activities will nourish and soothe them? Write down your self-care goals for the month. They could include reducing stress, boosting self-esteem, or improving your emotional well-being.

1._____

2._____

3._____

4._____

5._____

- **Daily commitment:** Commit to doing at least one self-care activity every day. It doesn't have to be something elaborate; even small gestures count. The key is consistency.
- **Variety is the spice of life:** Ensure that your self-care activities encompass various aspects of your well-being. Mix in activities that address your emotional, physical, and mental needs. This variety will help you heal and grow holistically.
- **Plan ahead:** Take a few minutes at the beginning of each week to schedule your self-care activities. This way, you can ensure that they fit into your daily routine.
- **Accountability:** Share your self-care calendar with a trusted friend or support group. Having someone to encourage and hold you accountable can be incredibly motivating.
- **Reflect and adjust:** At the end of each day, take a moment to reflect on how the self-care activity made you feel. Did it bring you joy, relaxation, or peace? If not, don't be afraid to adjust your calendar to better suit your needs.
- **Adapt and evolve:** As you progress through the 30 days, you may discover new self-care activities that

resonate with you. Feel free to adapt and evolve your calendar to reflect these changes.

INNER CHILD JOURNAL PROMPTS

Here are five journal prompts tailored to inner child healing, with a focus on self-care:

- **Exploring your inner sanctuary:** Imagine a safe, nurturing place where your inner child can feel completely at ease. Describe this sanctuary in vivid detail – what does it look like, smell like, and feel like? How do you nurture your inner child within this sanctuary? Write about how you can access and revisit this place whenever you need to comfort and care for your inner child.

_____

_____

_____

_____

_____

- **Your inner child's self-care wish list:** If your inner child could express their needs and desires for self-care, what would be on their wish list? List at least five specific self-care activities, no matter how simple or extravagant they may be. Then, commit to incorporating one of these activities into your daily or weekly routine, just as you would for a beloved child.

1. _____
2. _____
3. _____
4. _____
5. _____

- **Creating a self-care menu:** Imagine you have a menu of self-care activities; each designed to soothe and nurture your inner child. Create this menu by listing a variety of self-care practices that resonate with you, such as meditation, journaling, art, nature walks, or listening to soothing music. Next to each item, specify how it directly benefits your inner child. Whenever you need self-care, consult this menu and choose an activity that aligns with your inner child's needs in that moment.

1. _____
2. _____
3. _____
4. _____
5. _____

- **The magic of boundaries:** Recall a recent instance where you felt overwhelmed or taken advantage of by someone else's demands or expectations. How did this experience trigger your inner wounded child? What boundaries could you have set to protect and nurture yourself in that situation? Describe how you plan to assertively establish these boundaries moving forward.

_____

_____

_____

_____

_____

- **The self-care compass:** Create a self-care compass with four directions: Emotional, Physical, Mental, and Spiritual. Under each direction, list three self-care activities or practices that resonate with you. Commit to incorporating these self-care strategies into your daily or weekly routine to nurture your inner child's healing journey.

Emotional:

1. _____
2. _____   **Physical:**
3. _____

                                    1. _____
                                    _____
                                    2. _____
Mental: _____
                                    3. _____
1. _____   _____

2. _____

                                    Spiritual:
3. _____
                                    1. _____
_____   2. _____
                                    3. _____

In this chapter, we've explored the invaluable process of adapting positive coping mechanisms. Allowing us to foster self-awareness and cultivate adaptive strategies, we've laid the foundation for personal growth, inner child healing, and emotional resilience.

As we transition into the next chapter, we will explore the need to reconnect with our inner child. Building on the positive coping mechanisms we've developed, we will look at the healing potential of re-establishing a nurturing relationship with our younger selves, uncovering layers of emotional under-standing, and unlocking a path to profound self-discovery and inner healing.

6

RECONNECTING WITH YOUR INNER CHILD

You just have to surround yourself with the things that make you grateful to be alive.

— JUANSEN DIZON

This chapter is not just about understanding your past; it's about actively engaging with it and nurturing the wounded aspects of your childhood self. We will use a blend of activities, creative exercises, and self-reflection to help you reconnect with the inner child who has been waiting patiently for your attention.

Your inner child is the pure, unadulterated essence of who you were before the world began to layer expectations, wounds, and defenses upon you. This chapter is all about giving that inner child the love, care, and attention it deserves. The goal here is to foster a deeper connection between your adult self and your inner child, ultimately leading to a more integrated and authentic you.

As you start this journey, I want you to ponder a question that will be a guiding light throughout this chapter: What elements of your childhood still bring you a sense of wonder and gratitude, and how can you incorporate them into your daily life? Your inner child holds the key to rediscovering the joy, curiosity, and authenticity that you may have lost along the way. By honoring and reconnecting with that inner child, you can infuse your present life with renewed vitality and a profound sense of self.

HEALING AND NURTURING YOUR INNER CHILD

Before we dive into the practical activities, let's begin by understanding the importance of connecting with your inner child. This is the foundation upon which your healing journey is built. Your inner child holds the key to unlocking the wounds of your past and nurturing them with love and compassion.

Activity 1: The Inner Child Letter

Start by finding a quiet, comfortable space. Take a deep breath and close your eyes. Imagine your inner child, the little version of you from your past. Write a letter to this child. Tell them that you see them, that you love them, and that you're here to take care of them now. Be as nurturing and empathetic as possible. Let your inner child know that they are safe with you.

Activity 2: Exploring Your Childhood in Photos

Let's journey back in time by gathering some cherished photos from your childhood. Spend time perusing these snapshots of the past, allowing the moments captured to wash over you. Pay attention to the emotions that well up within you and the memories that come to the surface. Take a moment to reflect. This exercise is a gentle way to connect with the experiences of your younger self, fostering empathy and understanding.

Activity 3: Embrace the Joy of Messiness

Grant yourself the freedom to revel in the sheer delight of creating a beautiful mess while engaging in an activity you love, be it baking, painting, experimenting with makeup, or playing with Play-Doh. Although you'll need to tidy up afterward, the liberating experience of letting go and embracing the mess is well worth it. This activity invites you to connect with your inner child's sense of spontaneity and creativity.

Activity 4: Cultivate Your Safe Haven

Designate a physical space within your home as your personal sanctuary. Decorate it with items that evoke feelings of security and comfort. Whenever life becomes overwhelming, retreat to this safe space, take deep breaths, and reconnect with your inner child. In this haven, you can find solace and nurturing, just as a caring guardian would provide.

Activity 5: Visualization—Reuniting With Your Inner Child

Close your eyes and embark on a guided visualization journey. Imagine yourself strolling down a serene path, leading you into a lush and enchanting forest. Within this natural haven, you encounter a young version of yourself, playing alone. Approach your inner child with kindness, introduce yourself, and extend a hand of friendship. Inquire if your inner child would like to accompany you on this profound healing journey. This exercise helps you forge a compassionate connection with your inner child, offering support and companionship.

Activity 6: Exploring Your Childhood Journey

Let's embark on a journey down memory lane by creating a timeline of your life, highlighting significant events from your childhood. As you do, take a moment to contemplate how these events have shaped you and influenced your inner child. This exercise offers valuable insights into your past and can help you better understand the wounds that may need healing.

Activity 7: Embrace Playful Delights

Sometimes, it's important to treat yourself to something delightfully absurd or whimsical. Whether it's savoring an ice cream cone as colossal as your head or discovering a stuffed animal that tugs at your heartstrings, give in to these "silly" pleasures. They have the magical power to reignite the unadulterated joy reminiscent of childhood Christmas mornings. Be it bouncing in a bounce house, hosting a whimsical fairy-themed party, climbing a tree, or trying a new side of the bed, these moments can infuse your life with a comforting warmth.

Activity 8: Nurture Your Inner Child Through Journaling

Begin an inner child journal where you can pen letters, stories, or reflections from the perspective of your inner child. This practice is a precious way to gain a deeper understanding of your inner child's needs and provide the nurturing and care they deserve.

Activity 9: Reenact the Joyous Past

Select a cherished childhood photo that captures a moment of pure happiness. Recreate that moment in the present as faithfully as you can, even if it involves revisiting a simple childhood game or activity. By reconnecting with these joyful memories, you honor your inner child's spirit and invite warmth and nostalgia into your life.

Activity 10: Affirming Your Inner Child

Let's create a list of affirmations that lovingly address the needs and fears of your inner child. These daily affirmations will serve as a source of reassurance and unwavering support, just like a caring parent would provide.

Activity 11: Authentic Expression

Children often speak their minds without filters, and while we may not entirely abandon our filters, we can practice being more honest about our feelings. Begin by taking small steps, like expressing your restaurant preferences or respectfully declining a social invitation when rest is needed. This exercise allows you to honor your authentic self and build the courage to speak your truth.

Activity 12: Gentle Nature Stroll

Take a leisurely nature walk, not focused on reaching a destination but on truly connecting with the natural world. Choose a local park or trail, and savor the experience of exploring at a relaxed pace. Pause to admire the beauty of flowers, soak in scenic views, or listen to the melodies of the birds. Let nature nurture your inner child's sense of wonder.

Activity 13: Playtime With Kids

Few things can reignite your connection with your inner child, quite like spending time with children. Offer to engage in imaginative play with your nieces, nephews, or your friends' children the next time they require a babysitter. Engaging in their world of imagination and play will rekindle the youthful spirit within you.

Activity 14: Revisit Childhood Reads

Visit your local library and pick up a beloved childhood book like *Junie B. Jones* or *Ramona and Beezus*. Allow yourself the pleasure of an easy, nostalgic read. As you dive into the pages, those cherished memories of your initial encounters with these stories will come flooding back, enveloping you in the warmth of your inner child's world.

Activity 15: Release Pent-Up Emotions

When was the last time you intentionally allowed yourself to express your frustrations and anger? Sometimes, it's liberating to break away from the constraints of adulthood. Find a safe outlet for these emotions, whether it's tearing up paper, throwing ice cubes at the sidewalk, or giving your pillow a good punch. This physical release can provide a sense of relief and help you reconnect with the emotions that may have been buried for too long.

Activity 16: Rediscover the Joy of Sleepovers

Instead of the usual coffee meet-ups, why not plan a delightful sleepover with your closest friends? Stay up late snacking, build pillow forts, watch movies, and engage in heartfelt conversations. This experience allows you to rekindle the carefree spirit of your inner teenager while strengthening the bonds of friendship. Trust me; it'll be a memorable and cherished time for everyone involved.

Activity 17: Cultivate Mindfulness and Meditation

Mindfulness exercises offer a gentle path to exploring your subconscious thoughts and emotions. As you practice, reflect on your most vivid childhood memories and identify moments in your present life when those same feelings arise. Alternatively, if guided meditations aren't your preference, try a soothing sound bathing exercise. These practices can help you reconnect with your inner self, fostering empathy and understanding.

Activity 18: Dance Freely Around Your Home

Put on your favorite music and let yourself dance with abandon throughout your home. Remember, there's no audience judging your moves! Dancing is a wonderful way to reconnect with your body and release any pent-up nervous energy. Plus, it's an absolute blast!

Activity 19: Gift Yourself Laughter

When tension starts to weigh you down, treat yourself to some well-deserved laughter therapy. Put on your favorite funny movie or watch that YouTube video that never fails to tickle your funny bone. Just as we sometimes suppress our anger, we also tend to downplay our joy. Give yourself the precious gift of laughter; it's a powerful antidote to life's stresses.

Activity 20: Embrace Volunteering

When was the last time you dedicated your time to something purely for the joy of giving? Consider finding a local charity or community organization that resonates with your values and volunteer a few days each month. This act of selflessness can be a beautiful way to reconnect with the pure-hearted spirit of your inner child.

Activity 21: Rediscover Childhood Passions

Think back to those carefree days of your childhood. Did you spend endless weekends exploring the world of backyard bugs, mastering the art of hula hooping, or playing the piano with unbridled enthusiasm? It's time to rekindle those passions as an adult. Reconnect with your inner child by picking up an old hobby or interest. Find joy in revisiting something that once brought you pure delight.

Activity 22: Nurture Daydreams and Visualization

In our fast-paced, screen-dominated world, the art of daydreaming and visualization often takes a back seat. Allow yourself the gift of intentional boredom. Find a quiet corner, sit, and let your mind wander freely. Rediscover the magic of imagination and creativity. If you struggle to find time for daydreaming, consider creating more space for it in your life. Your inner child thrives on the beauty of unstructured thinking.

Activity 23: Reconnect With Childhood Tastes

Do you recall the delectable flavors of your favorite childhood meal, the one that filled you with anticipation and warmth? Treat yourself to that cherished dish as an adult. Prepare it at home, accompanied by your favorite music, or take yourself on a solo dinner date to savor the nostalgia. By indulging in this culinary journey, you're not just satisfying your taste buds; you're nurturing your inner child's longing for comfort and familiarity.

CREATIVE EXPRESSION

Oscar Wilde once said, "Man is least himself when he talks in his own person. Give him a mask, and he will tell you the truth (Kaimal, 2020)." Creative expression serves as a bridge between the past and the present, allowing you to process and release emotions that may have been suppressed for years. It's like opening a door to your heart and soul, giving your inner child a safe space to be heard, seen, and felt. This is an essential part of reparenting and nurturing the wounded inner child within you.

Here are 20 unique and inspiring ideas for creative outlets that will help you tap into your inner child's emotions and experiences:

1. **Journaling:** Begin with a simple daily journal to jot down your thoughts and feelings.
2. **Art therapy:** Use paint, pastels, or colored pencils to express your emotions visually.

3. **Letter writing:** Write a letter from your adult self to your inner child, or vice versa.

4. **Collage making:** Create collages with images that resonate with your inner child.

5. **Photography:** Capture moments and scenes that evoke emotions within you.

6. **Sculpting:** Mold clay or playdough into shapes that represent your feelings.

7. **Dancing:** Move your body freely to music, letting your emotions flow through dance.

8. **Creative writing:** Craft poems, short stories, or essays about your inner child's experiences.

9. **Music composition:** Write songs or melodies that express your emotions.

10. **Nature art:** Use leaves, flowers, and rocks to create temporary outdoor art.

11. **Mandala drawing:** Create intricate mandalas that reflect your inner world.

12. **Coloring books:** Find adult coloring books with intricate designs to color mindfully.

13. **Gardening:** Cultivate a garden to nurture your connection with nature.

14. **Cooking and baking:** Prepare dishes that evoke comforting childhood memories.

15. **Photomontage:** Create a visual story with your own photographs and images.

16. **Scrapbooking:** Compile a scrapbook filled with mementos and memories.

17. **Dream journaling:** Record your dreams and explore their symbolism.

18. **Voice Recording:** Speak your thoughts, feelings, or stories into a recorder.
19. **Puppetry:** Use puppets to act out and express your inner child's experiences.
20. **Outdoor adventures:** Explore hiking, camping, or other outdoor activities to connect with your inner child's sense of wonder.

Remember, the goal here is not to create a masterpiece but to tap into your emotions and provide an outlet for your inner child's voice. Be patient and compassionate with yourself during this process. Creative expression can sometimes stir up intense feelings, but that's part of the healing journey.

Now, I encourage you to choose at least one of these creative outlets and incorporate it into your healing routine. Allow your inner child to express themselves freely, and as you do, you'll find yourself developing a deeper understanding of your past, improved emotional regulation, and a growing sense of self. You've got this!

FORGIVENESS AND ACCEPTANCE

In this section, we'll explore the transformative power of forgiveness and acceptance. These are crucial steps in nurturing your wounded inner child and paving the way for lasting healing and personal growth.

Forgiving Yourself

Let's begin by addressing self-forgiveness. Many of us carry the weight of past mistakes, regrets, and self-blame. It's time to release that burden and provide your inner child with the love and understanding they deserve. Here's how to start:

- **Self-compassion:** Begin by acknowledging that everyone makes mistakes; it's a part of being human. Embrace self-compassion by speaking kindly to yourself. Replace harsh self-criticism with words of understanding and encouragement.
- **Reflection and ownership:** Reflect on the actions or choices that still weigh on your conscience. Take responsibility for them without judgment. Understand that your past actions don't define your worth as a person.
- **Learn and grow:** The essence of forgiveness is not just about letting go but also about learning and growing from your past. What lessons have you gained from your mistakes? How can you apply these lessons to your present and future?

- **Affirmations:** Write down positive affirmations that affirm your self-worth and ability to change. Repeat them daily, reinforcing your commitment to self-forgiveness.

_____

_____

_____

_____

_____

_____

_____

Forgiving Others (Without Actually Talking to Them)

Forgiving others is a complex and personal journey. Sometimes, we may not be able to or have the desire to communicate with those who have hurt us. Here's how to navigate this process:

- **Understand your feelings:** Begin by acknowledging your emotions. What are the specific grievances or wounds caused by others? Understand that forgiveness is about your healing, not absolving their actions.

_____

_____

_____

- **Empathy and perspective:** Try to see the situation from the other person's perspective. This doesn't justify their actions but helps you grasp their motivations and pain, which can be liberating. For example, a woman grew up in a toxic and dysfunctional family. Her mother was a narcissist, and despite this, she sought her approval well into her 40s. She would make the difficult decision to end their relationship when she turned 50. While working to heal her inner child, she felt the need to forgive her mother. She looked at years of her childhood from her mother's perspective. She came to see her mother suffers from mental illness and could forgive some of her decisions. This didn't mean she was able to reconnect or move forward with her. This meant she was able to see one piece of the puzzle. This allowed her to release guilt and blame and send it back to her mother.
- **Release the resentment:** Holding onto anger and resentment only continues to hurt you. Visualize releasing this negativity as if you're unburdening yourself.
- **Boundaries:** Forgiveness doesn't mean forgetting or allowing someone to harm you again. Set clear boundaries to protect yourself moving forward.

Forgiving Your Parents—A Healing Exercise

Forgiving our parents can be one of the most challenging aspects of inner child healing. However, it's also one of the most liberating. Here's a practical exercise to help you work through this process:

Step 1: Reflect on Your Feelings

Take some time to sit quietly and reflect on your relationship with your parents. Write down any feelings of anger, hurt, or disappointment that come to mind.

_____

_____

_____

_____

_____

Step 2: Empathize

Try to see your parents as individuals who may have had their own struggles and wounds. Consider the circumstances they faced when you were a child. What challenges did they experience?

_____

_____

_____

_____

_____

_____

_____

Step 3: Write a Letter (Unsent)

Write a letter to your parents expressing your feelings and your decision to forgive them. Pour your heart into it, but remember, this letter doesn't need to be sent. It's for your healing.

_____

_____

_____

_____

_____

_____

_____

_____

_____

_____

Step 4: Ritual of Release

Find a safe and quiet space to perform a ritual of release. Read your letter aloud, imagining that you are releasing the pain and resentment associated with your parents. You can even burn the letter symbolically, letting go of the past.

Be patient with yourself and allow your inner child the space to heal gradually. By practicing forgiveness and acceptance, you're nurturing the wounded parts of yourself and moving closer to a healthier, more resilient you.

EXERCISE: 30-DAY NURTURING AND WRITING FOR YOUR INNER CHILD

Let's embark on this journey of self-discovery and healing. Remember, it's about progress, not perfection. Each day, take a moment to connect with your inner child and give them the love and support they deserve.

Day 1: Connecting With Your Inner Child

- Find a cozy, tranquil space where you can truly relax. Take a few deep, soothing breaths in and out, allowing yourself to settle into the present moment.
- Now, gently close your eyes and picture your younger self. See them clearly in your mind's eye, their age, their appearance, and sense the emotions they carried. Remember the innocence, the vulnerability, and the dreams of that younger version of you.
- With a heart full of compassion, write a heartfelt letter to your inner child, letting them know just how much you love and care for them. Pour your love onto the pages, and as you write, make a promise—a commitment to their healing and happiness. Tell them that you're here now, with open arms, ready to nurture and protect them like they deserved all along.

_____
_____
_____
_____
_____
_____
_____
_____
_____
_____

Day 2: Childhood Memories

- Recall a joyful childhood memory.
- Write about it in detail, reliving the moment. What sights, sounds, and smells do you remember?
- Reflect on how this memory makes you feel now.

_____
_____
_____
_____
_____
_____
_____

Day 3: Embracing Vulnerability

- Write about a time when you felt vulnerable as a child.
- Explore your emotions and fears from that moment.
- Offer words of comfort and reassurance to your inner child, acknowledging their pain.

_____

_____

_____

_____

_____

_____

_____

Day 4: Self-Compassion

- Reflect on your inner critic's voice. What harsh judgments do you often hear?
- Write a compassionate response to these judgments, as if speaking to your inner child.
- Encourage self-kindness and understanding.

_____

_____

_____

_____

_____

_____

_____

Day 5: Imaginary Safe Haven

- Create an imaginary, safe place where your inner child can go whenever they need comfort.
- Describe this place in vivid detail: colors, textures, and all the senses.
- Write about how this safe haven makes your inner child feel.

_____

_____

_____

_____

_____

_____

_____

Day 6: Reparenting Commitment

- Reaffirm your commitment to reparenting your inner child.
- Write a list of nurturing actions you'll take for the next 30 days.
- Include self-care activities, affirmations, or promises to your inner child.

_____

_____

_____

_____

_____

_____

_____

Day 7: Healing Through Forgiveness

- Reflect on any past hurts or resentments from your childhood.
- Write a letter of forgiveness to those who may have caused you pain.
- Emphasize that forgiving is a gift to yourself, releasing you from the burden of the past.

_____

_____

_____

_____

_____

_____

_____

_____

_____

Day 8: Inner Child's Needs

- List the emotional needs your inner child may not have had met.
- Reflect on how these unmet needs may have influenced your adult life.
- Commit to meeting these needs for your inner child moving forward.

_____

_____

_____

_____

_____

_____

_____

Day 9: Journal of Emotions

- Start a journal specifically for your inner child.
- Write down any emotions that surface throughout the day.
- Reflect on how these emotions might be connected to your past experiences.

_____

_____

_____
_____
_____
_____
_____

Day 10: Revisiting Old Photos

- Look through old family photos or memorabilia.
- Write about the emotions and memories that arise as you explore your past.
- Share any insights about your inner child's experiences.

_____
_____
_____
_____
_____
_____
_____

Day 11: Inner Child's Voice

- Listen to your inner child's voice within you.
- Write a dialogue between your adult self and your inner child. Ask them how they're feeling and what they need.
- Offer comfort and support as you engage in this inner conversation.

_____
_____
_____
_____
_____
_____
_____

Day 12: Embracing Playfulness

- Reconnect with your playful side.
- Engage in a fun and childlike activity, such as drawing, coloring, or playing a game.
- Write about the joy and freedom you experience during this playtime.

_____
_____
_____
_____
_____
_____
_____

Day 13: Gratitude for Growth

- Reflect on the progress you've made so far in nurturing your inner child.

- Write down three things you're grateful for regarding your inner child healing journey.
- Acknowledge the positive changes you've noticed within yourself.

_____

_____

_____

_____

_____

_____

_____

Day 14: Setting Boundaries

- Explore any areas in your life where you need to establish healthy boundaries.
- Write down your boundaries and how they will protect and nurture your inner child.
- Commit to enforcing these boundaries with love and assertiveness.

_____

_____

_____

_____

_____

_____

_____

Day 15: Celebrating Progress

- Celebrate the halfway point of your 30-day journey.
- Write a letter to yourself, acknowledging the growth and healing you've experienced.
- Express your pride and love for your inner child and your commitment to continuing this transformative journey.

_____

_____

_____

_____

_____

_____

_____

Keep engaging with these daily exercises, reflecting on your experiences and nurturing your inner child. For the remaining 15 days, choose the ones that resonate with you most. By the end of this 30-day journey, you'll have developed a stronger, more compassionate relationship with yourself and gained valuable tools for ongoing personal growth and emotional resilience. Stay committed to the process, and remember that you are doing important work to heal and nurture your inner child.

INNER CHILD JOURNAL PROMPTS

The Wise Nurturer Within

- Close your eyes and visualize yourself as a loving, nurturing parent or mentor.
- Write a letter from this wise nurturer to your inner child. Offer guidance, encouragement, and unconditional love.
- Imagine this inner nurturer always by your side, supporting you through your healing process. Describe how their presence feels and how they empower your inner child.

- **Nurturing self-talk**: Pay attention to your inner dialogue throughout the day. Write down any negative or critical self-talk you notice. Then, rewrite those statements with compassionate, loving, and supportive words as if you were speaking to your inner child. How does this shift in self-talk make you feel?

_____

_____

_____

_____

_____

_____

_____

- **Dear inner child, today I...**: Write a letter from your present self to your inner child, describing a specific action or choice you made today that you believe would make your inner child proud or feel safe. Reflect on the significance of this action and how it connects to your healing journey.

_____

_____

_____

_____

_____

_____

_____

_____

_____

_____

- **Color your emotions**: Choose a color that represents an emotion you're currently feeling or have felt recently. Create an abstract artwork using this color, allowing your emotions to guide your strokes and shapes. Write about the process and what your inner child might say about this expression of emotion.

_____

_____

_____

_____

_____

_____

_____

- **Rewriting your inner narrative**: Identify a recurring negative belief or self-criticism that stems from your childhood experiences. Write down this belief and the circumstances that contributed to its development. Now, challenge this belief by writing a compassionate, empowering alternative narrative. How can you reframe this belief to better support your growth and self-acceptance?

_____

_____

_____

_____

_____

_____

_____

In this chapter, we covered the importance of integrating the lessons and practices of reconnecting with the inner child into daily life. The next chapter will focus on sustaining the progress made and applying these insights to future challenges and growth.

7

MOVING FORWARD AND MAINTAINING PROGRESS

Great is the human who has not lost his childlike heart.

— MENCIUS

Remember that healing your inner child is not a one-time fix as you progress; it's an ongoing process. Your inner child will continue to evolve and grow, just as you do. It's like tending to a garden—you've planted the seeds, nurtured the soil, and seen the first blooms of recovery. Now, it's time to ensure that your garden thrives for years to come.

In this final chapter, we'll focus on applying the insights and techniques you've acquired to set meaningful goals and plan for long-term success. I'll equip you with tools to maintain your progress and continue your journey of personal growth and self-improvement.

Maintaining your childlike heart is not about naivety; it's about preserving the pure essence of wonder, curiosity, and authenticity that resides within you. Life can throw its share of challenges and joys your way, and it's in these moments that your inner child becomes your greatest ally. They remind you of the resilience, creativity, and boundless potential that exists within you.

So, as you reflect on your journey, ponder this question: How can maintaining a childlike heart help you in navigating the challenges and joys of your adult life? The answer lies within you, and it's a powerful source of strength and wisdom.

In the pages ahead, we'll explore strategies to ensure that your inner child continues to thrive, supporting you as you face the world with renewed confidence and self-compassion. It's time to take what you've learned and use it as a foundation for a lifetime of growth, healing, and fulfillment.

Let's start this final leg of your journey together. You've come so far, and there's an exciting path ahead—one filled with personal growth, emotional resilience, and the beauty of a well-nurtured inner child guiding you every step of the way.

SETTING GOALS FOR THE FUTURE

Let's have a heartfelt conversation about the incredible importance of setting goals in maintaining your inner child healing.

Sometimes, we don't fully grasp just how vital these goals are as we navigate through life's twists and turns.

But here's the thing: goal setting isn't a mundane chore; it's a path. The benefits it brings are profound and life-changing.

When you set goals, you're not just planning your direction; you're sparking a change within yourself. Goals trigger new behaviors, help you concentrate, and give you the push you need to move forward in life.

They offer you more than just guidance; they help you focus on aligning your goals and nurturing a feeling of control over your own future. You see, you can't control what you don't track, and you can't enhance something you don't effectively control. Setting goals empowers you to achieve all of this and more.

Let's take a moment to discuss procrastination. It's common to focus on the present rather than the future, but this can sometimes hinder our progress. Putting off important steps toward our goals can delay our journey to healing.

Remember, setting goals is a journey of growth and change. The goals you set in your 20s may be different from those you set in your 50s. It's not about age; what really counts is your dedication to regularly reviewing and updating your life goals with care and compassion.

Setting goals isn't just something you think about; it really affects how you act and perform. It gives you energy, making you work harder and stick with things longer. This makes you want to come up with plans to achieve your goals, which then makes you feel satisfied and even more motivated.

When it comes to mental health, setting goals can make a world of difference. Many of us have experienced the daunting feeling of being overwhelmed when we think about the mental health challenges we want to address. It can feel like we're heading straight for a waterfall when we start listing them all out. However, learning to set goals can help break down these overwhelming barriers, making our healing journey feel more manageable.

This is exactly why CBT is a great tool for healing our inner child. Setting goals is a major part of its foundation. Many studies have shown that individuals who set goals are more likely to accept help for their mental health (Riopel, 2019).

Remember, setting goals is not about overwhelming yourself with an endless to-do list. It's about taking control of your well-being step by step. It gives you direction, prioritizes what truly matters, and keeps you accountable, even when setbacks occur.

While we cherish moments of spontaneity and leisure, those with well-defined goals often find even greater enjoyment in their downtime. Goals enrich our lives and allow us to create the life we truly desire.

Steps to Set Achievable Goals

Setting achievable goals is a crucial step in your personal growth and healing journey. It's like mapping out the path to the treasure within yourself. Let's walk through some steps and tips to help you set and achieve those goals:

Step 1: Reflect on Your Inner Child

Begin by taking a moment to connect with your inner child. Think about what they need and what areas of your life require healing. It's essential to have a clear understanding of your emotional wounds and past experiences to set relevant goals.

Step 2: Define Your Goals

Start small. Begin with one or two specific goals that align with your inner child's needs. Make sure your goals are SMART (Leonard & Watts, 2022):

- **Specific:** Clearly define what you want to achieve.
- **Measurable:** Set clear criteria to track your progress.
- **Achievable:** Ensure your goals are realistic and within your capabilities.
- **Relevant:** Align your goals with your inner child's healing needs.
- **Time-Bound:** Set a timeframe to work within.

For example, instead of a vague goal like "I want to heal," make it specific, like "I want to work on my fear of rejection by practicing self-compassion exercises for 20 minutes every day for the next month."

Step 3: Break It Down

When you set a significant goal, whether it's related to your inner child healing journey or any other aspect of your life, it can often feel daunting and overwhelming. The key to making your goals more manageable and achievable is to break them down into smaller, digestible steps. This is a crucial step in the process, as it transforms your goal from a vague idea into a concrete action plan.

- **Divide your goal:** The first part of this step involves dissecting your overarching goal into smaller components. Imagine your goal as a puzzle, and these smaller steps are the individual pieces that, when put together, will form the complete picture. Breaking your goal down in this way allows you to see the specific tasks and actions required to achieve it.

- **Make it manageable:** By breaking your goal into smaller steps, you prevent it from feeling overwhelming. This is particularly important in the context of inner child healing, as it can be a complex and emotionally charged journey. These manageable steps help you focus on one piece of the puzzle at a time, reducing anxiety and making the process more achievable.

Step 4: Create Accountability

Share your goals with a trusted friend, family member, mentor, or a supportive community or group. Having someone who can hold you accountable and provide encouragement can make a big difference in your success journey. This accountability partner can help you stay on track, offer valuable insights, and celebrate your achievements with you, making the process more enjoyable and rewarding."

Step 5: Stay Consistent

Consistency is key to making progress on your healing journey. Set aside dedicated time for your healing work each day or week, and commit to sticking to your schedule, even on days when you might not feel like it. Remember, healing is a journey, and every step you take counts toward your progress.

Here are some expanded tips for success:

- **Stay patient and compassionate:** Setbacks are a natural part of the process. It's important to be kind and patient with yourself, just as you would with your inner child. Self-compassion is a powerful tool for growth and healing.
- **Track your progress:** Keeping a journal to record your thoughts, emotions, and progress can be incredibly beneficial. Not only does it provide a space for self-reflection, but it also allows you to track your growth over time. This can help you stay motivated and gain a deeper understanding of your journey.
- **Celebrate:** It's essential to acknowledge and celebrate your achievements, no matter how small they may seem. Celebrating your progress boosts your motivation and self-esteem, reinforcing the positive changes you're making in your life.
- **Adjust as needed:** If you find that a goal isn't working or needs modification, don't be afraid to adjust it. Flexibility is key to success, and being open to adapting your goals and strategies can lead to more effective outcomes. Embracing change and being willing to

adjust your approach can help you stay on the path to success.

Remember, you have the strength and resilience within you to heal and grow. Your inner child deserves the love and care you're giving them. Keep moving forward, one step at a time, and you'll see the positive changes in your life as you build a healthier, happier relationship with yourself and others.

PLANNING FOR LONG-TERM SUCCESS

Creating a long-term strategy for maintaining emotional health and well-being is vital for long-term success. Let's focus on building resilience, reducing stress, getting good quality sleep, strengthening social connections, coping with loss, and embracing mindfulness.

Nurturing Your Ongoing Resilience

Resilience is like a precious treasure that you can nurture and expand over time. Let's explore how to sustain and enhance your emotional well-being, always keeping progress in mind.

- **Holistic self-care:** Continue to nurture your inner child's physical well-being by maintaining healthy habits. Ensure you are eating well, staying physically active, and getting regular sleep. These habits are the solid foundation upon which your emotional well-being thrives.

- **Daily moments of joy:** Dedicate time each day to honor and celebrate your progress. Prioritize self-care by acknowledging the good moments and engaging in activities that bring you joy. Remember, this is not self-indulgence; it's essential for your emotional health and well-being.

- **Evolving perspectives:** Keep encouraging yourself to look at life's challenges from different angles. Continue to embrace challenges as opportunities for personal growth. Cherish the lessons learned from your past, and maintain your focus on the positive aspects of life.

- **Ongoing gratitude practice:** Cultivate a daily practice of gratitude to sustain your positive outlook. Regularly take a moment to acknowledge and express gratitude for the blessings in your life. This practice will continue to shift your perspective and bolster your emotional resilience.

- **Reflect and refine:** Engage in regular self-reflection on the values and principles of your inner child. Continuously examining these will help you improve and reinforce the fundamental beliefs that shape your life, which is crucial for maintaining your emotional well-being.

- **Continuous connection:** Surround yourself with the warmth and positivity of those who support your progress. Lean on your network of positive, healthy individuals who encourage your growth. Never hesitate to seek their support when needed, as they are essential to your ongoing success.

Nurturing Stress Reduction Practices

Stress is a natural part of life, but chronic stress can hinder your growth and well-being. Let's explore strategies to not only reduce stress but also sustain your progress on the path to emotional healing.

- **Prioritizing restful sleep:** Continue to make sleep a non-negotiable part of your daily routine. Adequate sleep is not just crucial for clear thinking but also plays a significant role in maintaining emotional balance. Consistency in your sleep patterns will help you sustain progress.
- **Regular physical activity:** Remember that physical activity remains a cornerstone in your stress reduction journey. Aim to incorporate 30 minutes of daily exercise, which will not only boost your mood but also continue to reduce stress. Find enjoyable activities that keep you active, and make them a lasting habit.
- **Prioritizing your tasks:** As you move forward, continue to set priorities in your life. Understand what requires immediate attention and what can wait. Learning to say no to overwhelming tasks is a skill that will help you manage stress effectively and sustain your progress.
- **Self-compassion:** Keep practicing self-compassion on a daily basis. Reflect on your achievements rather than dwelling on what remains undone. Treat yourself as your own best friend, nurturing your inner child with kindness and understanding.

- **Mindful relaxation:** Maintain your commitment to activities that promote relaxation and mindfulness, such as yoga or meditation. These practices, incorporating mindfulness and breathing exercises, are essential for managing stress in a sustainable way.
- **Seeking professional help:** Always remember that it's okay to reach out for support when stress becomes overwhelming. The path to healing doesn't have to be walked alone. Seek the guidance of a mental health professional if you find yourself struggling to manage stress effectively.

Nurturing Your Sleep Routine

Quality sleep is the cornerstone of both your mental and physical health, and it plays a significant role in maintaining your emotional well-being. Here are some great strategies to nurture your sleep routine:

- **Consistent sleep schedule:** Uphold the consistency of your sleep schedule. Continue to go to bed and wake up at the same time daily, as this practice helps regulate your body's internal clock and ensures a sustainable pattern of restful sleep.
- **Optimal sleep environment:** Keep your sleep environment comfortable, dark, and quiet. Maintaining these conditions supports the uninterrupted rest you need for sustained emotional well-being.
- **Regular exercise:** Maintain your commitment to regular physical activity. Exercise promotes better

sleep, but remember to avoid vigorous activities right before bedtime. By continuing this practice, you'll ensure ongoing progress in sleep quality.

- **Limiting electronics:** Stay mindful of your screen time before bed. Reduce exposure to blue light, as it can interfere with your sleep. Managing this aspect of your routine ensures continued progress in sleep quality.
- **Relaxation rituals:** Sustain your relaxation rituals before bedtime, such as reading or enjoying a warm bath. These activities help you wind down and signal to your body that it's time to rest.
- **Avoiding stimulants:** Continue to steer clear of stimulants like nicotine and caffeine in the hours leading up to bedtime. This practice safeguards your sleep and maintains your progress in achieving restorative rest.
- **Optimizing naps:** Keep daytime naps short and avoid them in the late afternoon. These habits ensure that your nighttime sleep remains restful and undisturbed.
- **Embracing natural light:** Spend time in natural sunlight during the day to regulate your sleep-wake cycle. This ongoing connection with natural light supports your overall sleep quality.

Deepening Nurturing Relationships

As you continue your inner child healing journey and maintain progress, nurturing your social connections remains a vital aspect of your emotional well-being. Relationships hold the power to profoundly impact your healing process. Let's look at some strategies to strengthen your social connections:

- **Strong bonds:** As you progress, continue to nurture strong connections with your loved ones, children, family, and friends. These deep and meaningful relationships are the bedrock of your emotional support system.
- **Promoting healthy habits:** Encourage your friends to develop healthy habits. Share activities that support the well-being of you and your loved ones. By consistently practicing these habits, you will make lasting progress in your emotional growth.
- **Participating in groups:** Maintain your involvement in groups that align with your interests, hobbies, or personal growth. These communities provide a sense of belonging and ongoing opportunities for connection and personal development.
- **Embracing volunteering:** Continue giving back to your community, as it creates a sense of purpose and strengthens your connections with others. Your volunteer work reinforces your commitment to personal growth and healing.
- **Exploring new frontiers:** Venture to different places, meet new people and continue to broaden your horizons. This spirit of adventure not only supports your personal growth but also strengthens your ability to connect with diverse individuals.

Self-Nurturing During Grief

As you continue your inner child healing journey and work toward maintaining progress, it's important to address the process of coping with loss. Grief is a natural part of life, and each person experiences it in their own unique way. Let's look at some strategies that not only help you navigate the grieving process but also support the lasting progress you've achieved in your inner child's healing.

- **Prioritizing self-care:** Just as you've prioritized self-care throughout your healing journey, continue to do so during times of loss. Maintain healthy habits that support your emotional well-being and provide a stable foundation for your inner child's healing.
- **Connecting with caring friends:** Continue to reach out to your friends when you're ready to talk. Don't isolate yourself during times of grief; the support of caring friends is invaluable in sustaining progress.
- **Engaging in grief support groups:** If you've found solace in grief support groups, consider remaining part of these communities. Connecting with others who share similar experiences of loss can provide ongoing comfort and a sense of belonging.
- **Avoiding hasty decisions:** As you move forward, remember the importance of refraining from making significant life changes immediately after a loss. Give yourself the time and space needed to heal and make decisions from a place of emotional stability.

- **Professional guidance:** If you find yourself struggling with daily activities or feeling overwhelmed by grief, don't hesitate to seek help from a mental health professional. Their support is invaluable in maintaining progress during challenging times.
- **Understanding the process:** Continue to remind yourself that mourning is a gradual process unique to each individual. It's entirely normal to experience a range of emotions during this journey. Be patient with yourself and your inner child as you both navigate the path of healing.

Nurturing Mindfulness in Daily Life

Embracing mindfulness remains a powerful tool for nurturing your emotional well-being. Remember, mindfulness is the practice of being present and fully aware of your thoughts, feelings, and surroundings. Let's explore strategies to not only incorporate mindfulness into your life but also to support the lasting progress you've achieved in your inner child's healing.

- **Deepening your breath:** Continue practicing deep breathing exercises to ground yourself and maintain a sense of calm throughout the day. Deep breaths are like anchors, keeping you connected to the present moment.
- **Walking mindfully:** Embrace the practice of mindful walking. Pay close attention to your breath, the sights, and the sounds as you take leisurely walks. This ongoing practice strengthens your ability to stay connected with the world around you.

- **Savoring each bite:** Keep savoring your meals with mindfulness. Be fully present and aware of the taste, textures, and aromas of your food. This practice ensures that you maintain progress in your mindful eating journey.
- **The body scan:** Continue to engage in the body scan exercise, mentally scanning your body from head to toe. This practice deepens your connection with physical sensations and helps you stay anchored in the present moment.
- **Expanding your mindfulness toolkit:** Explore a variety of mindfulness resources, including online programs and guided practices. These resources offer ongoing support for deepening your mindfulness journey and maintaining progress.

Remember that your path to inner child healing is an ongoing process, and these strategies will serve as a foundation for your long-term success. It's not always easy, but with commitment and practice, you will develop a healthier relationship with yourself and others, improved emotional regulation, and a stronger sense of self. You have the power to grow and continue to thrive.

INNER CHILD JOURNAL PROMPTS

- **Inner Child Self-Portrait:** Draw or paint a self-portrait of your inner child. Let your creativity flow without judgment or criticism. Afterward, write a narrative about this portrait, exploring the emotions, dreams, and aspirations your inner child holds. Reflect on how this artistic expression helps you connect with and understand your inner child on a deeper level.

- **Musical memory lane:** Select a song from your childhood that holds special meaning or memories. Write about the emotions, events, or people associated with that song. Consider how the lyrics, melody, or rhythm resonate with your inner child's experiences.

Listen to the song if you can and write about the feelings it evokes.

———————————————————————

———————————————————————

———————————————————————

———————————————————————

———————————————————————

- **Unsung heroes:** Recall moments from your childhood when someone unexpectedly showed you kindness, support, or love, even in a small way. Write about these unsung heroes and how their actions made a difference in your life. Reflect on the impact of these moments on your inner child and how they can inspire you to show similar kindness to yourself and others.

———————————————————————

———————————————————————

———————————————————————

———————————————————————

———————————————————————

- **Time capsule letter:** Pretend you're writing a letter to your future self, to be opened in five, ten, or twenty years. In this letter, share your current insights, challenges, and healing progress related to your inner child work. Offer words of encouragement and advice to your future self, and express your hopes and aspirations for your ongoing healing journey. Consider

what wisdom your future self might offer to your
present self.

_____

_____

_____

_____

_____

_____

_____

_____

_____

- **The imaginary tea party:** Imagine hosting a tea party
  with your inner child. Describe the setting, the
  conversation, and the activities that take place during
  this whimsical gathering. How does this imaginary tea
  party help you connect with your inner child's desires
  and emotions?

_____

_____

_____

_____

- **Unwrapping the gift of innocence:** Think of a gift you received as a child, whether it was a toy, a drawing, or something else. Describe this gift in detail and recall the joy it brought you. Now, consider the gift of innocence that your inner child holds within. How can you honor and protect this precious gift as an adult?

_____

_____

_____

_____

_____

This final chapter was dedicated to giving you tools and strategies to not only maintain but also continue your growth and commitment to healing your inner child. Continue to revisit this section when you need guidance or direction.

NO ONE WALKS THIS PATH ALONE

Not one of us walks this path alone – and you have a unique opportunity to help someone else realize that.

Simply by sharing your honest opinion of this book and a little about how it has helped you, you'll show new readers where they can find the guidance they need to begin their own healing journey.

WANT TO HELP OTHERS?

Your review can be a beacon of hope for someone who, like you, is seeking a path to self-discovery and personal growth.

Thank you so much for your support. We all need a guiding light sometimes, and your words will make a huge difference.

**Scan the QR Code to
Leave Your Review**

CONCLUSION

As we reach the end of this journey together, I want you to take a moment to reflect on how far you've come. The path of inner child healing is not always easy, but it's a journey worth taking.

In *A CBT Inner Child Workbook*, we've delved into some crucial and illuminating topics. I began by helping you identify and understand your inner child because acknowledging its influence on your present life is a monumental step in healing.

We then explored the foundations of CBT, a powerful tool that equips you with the skills needed to nurture your inner child. Childhood and generational trauma were unveiled, as we recognized that addressing the heart of these wounds is pivotal in the healing process.

Challenging negative beliefs, a vital component of CBT, was the next step in the journey of self-improvement. I would like to ask that you revisit this chapter whenever you find yourself trapped in those old, harmful patterns, as it will help you break free from their grip and move forward with a positive mindset.

We discussed coping mechanisms because we understand that healing can sometimes be overwhelming. Having the ability to cope with those difficult times can keep us motivated to move forward. Whenever life feels too much to bear, return to this section for guidance on navigating the storm.

We spent significant time reconnecting with your inner child and finding those moments of joy and positivity. I've provided you with tools and exercises to help you rediscover the light within you. I encourage you to revisit these sections as many times as necessary.

Finally, we wrapped up with a dedicated chapter on moving forward and maintaining progress. The ultimate goal is to live a life filled with happiness, joy, calm, and resilience in the face of challenges. Anytime you need a boost in motivation, spend some time reviewing this.

Throughout this journey, you've not only gained knowledge but also a deeper understanding of yourself. You've uncovered the wounds of your inner child and learned how to heal them. You've discovered the power of CBT, challenged negative beliefs, found coping strategies, and reconnected with your inner child's positivity.

Do you recall Christine from the introduction? She struggled with childhood trauma, and her story illustrated how this impacted her and her family gatherings. Her story would evolve over 20 years. Throughout that time, she would face denial and acceptance. When she was ready to reconnect with her inner child and heal, she leaned heavily on CBT.

She would utilize many strategies laid out in this workbook.

"When I began my healing journey, I struggled a lot with forgiveness. Trying to understand why those who were intended to love me would hurt me always caused confusion and hurt. Once I took the emotion out and looked at it from a different perspective, I was able to forgive."

It was important for Christine to accomplish this. At no point did she make room to allow those toxic family members back into her life. Forgiveness did not mean allowing the hurt to continue. It simply meant she was letting go of the burden she carried that no longer belonged to her. She envisioned it as a present she wrapped up and gave back to those who it belonged to.

"I still lean on tools to cope, heal, and grow. I journal every day and check in with my inner child. I talk openly to those I trust and hold myself accountable for self-care. I work on valuing myself every day."

Christine's story is a great example of how healing our inner child can often be looked at as a lifelong journey. This shouldn't be looked at as daunting, but instead, a gift you can give yourself. A gift of love, joy, strength, resilience, and courage.

So, as we conclude this journey, I urge you to embrace your path of self-discovery and growth through inner child work. Remember that every step you take toward healing and improvement is a step toward a more fulfilled and authentic life.

This workbook is designed to be your ongoing source of support. Believe in yourself, and let the healing begin. Your inner child deserves the love and care you've been giving it, and you deserve the happiness and peace that lie ahead.

With warmest wishes on your continued journey of healing and self-discovery,
Leigh W. Hart

Other Books You'll Love By

Leigh W. Hart

Don't Get Derailed By Your Attachment Style

Whether you are anxious, avoidant, or fearful in relationships, this book will provide you with proven strategies for effectively dealing with an insecure attachment style.

Reparenting Your Wounded Inner Child

Explore Childhood and Generational Trauma to Break Destructive Patterns, Build Emotional Strength and Achieve Personal Growth with 7 Empowering Steps. Free yourself from the pains of the past and create a life you will love now and in the future.

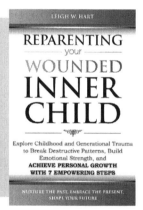

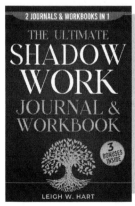

The Ultimate Shadow Work Journal & Workbook

A Comprehensive Collection of Exercises, Journal Prompts, and Affirmations for Profound Self-Discovery, Emotional Healing, and Personal Growth

Amazon.com/Author/LeighWHart

Elevate Your Journey With...

THREE COMPLIMENTARY SUPPORT WORKBOOKS!

Bonus #1

Customized Worksheets:

I have created a customized collection of **95+** journal pages and interactive worksheets that have been designed to complement the steps, journal prompts, and exercises discussed in this book perfectly.

Go to:

CBTInnerChild.LeighWHart.com

to receive your BONUS
printable support materials.

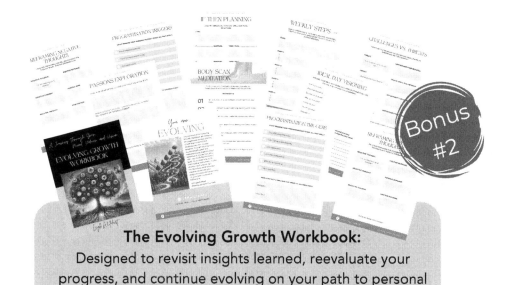

The Evolving Growth Workbook:

Designed to revisit insights learned, reevaluate your progress, and continue evolving on your path to personal fulfillment.

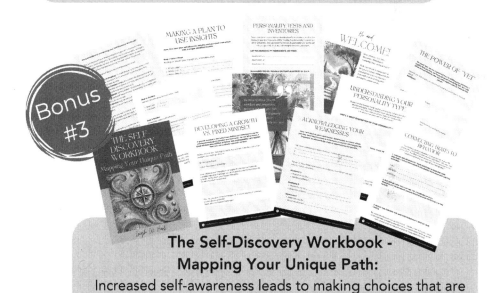

The Self-Discovery Workbook - Mapping Your Unique Path:

Increased self-awareness leads to making choices that are true to who you are. It helps you live and lead with purpose and authenticity.

Go to:

CBTInnerChild.LeighWHart.com

to receive your BONUS printable support materials.

The **CBT Inner Child Workbook** is a heartfelt follow-up and companion to my #1 Best Seller, **Reparenting Your Wounded Inner Child.**

I invite you to deepen your inner child healing journey by discovering the powerful techniques shared in **Reparenting Your Wounded Inner Child.** These resources work together to guide you towards greater self-compassion and emotional healing, providing transformative tools to care for and nurture your inner child.

Leigh W Hart

Amazon.com/Author/LeighWHart

REFERENCES

Alexa. (2023, February 3). *80 healing inner child quotes to feel validated*. Ambitiously Alexa. https://ambitiouslyalexa.com/healing-inner-child-quotes/

Austin, J. (2020, December 21). *Overlooked types of childhood trauma*. MadameNoire. https://madamenoire.com/1206375/overlooked-types-of-childhood-trauma/

Bachelard, G. (n.d.). *Gaston Bachelard quotes*. Goodreads. https://www.goodreads.com/quotes/9074117-so-like-a-forgotten-fire-a-childhood-can-always-flare

Bakr, A. (n.d.). *Childhood trauma*. Recognizetrauma.org. https://recognizetrauma.org/statistics.php

Breaking bad habits. (2017, June 28). NIH News in Health. https://newsinhealth.nih.gov/2012/01/breaking-bad-habits

Celestine, N. (2021, August 14). *What is behavior change in psychology? 5 models and theories*. PositivePsychology.com. https://positivepsychology.com/behavior-change/

Cognitive behavioral therapy CBT. (2018). CAMH. https://www.camh.ca/en/health-info/mental-illness-and-addiction-index/cognitive-behavioural-therapy

Cummings, E. E. (2001). *E. E. Cummings quotes*. BrainyQuote. https://www.brainyquote.com/quotes/e_e_cummings_161593

David, D., Cristea, I., & Hofmann, S. G. (2018). Why cognitive behavioral therapy is the current gold standard of psychotherapy. *Frontiers in Psychiatry*, *9*(4), 1–3. https://doi.org/10.3389/fpsyt.2018.00004

Demuth, M. (2019, September 6). *20 quotes on healing and doing the inner work*. Life Goals. https://lifegoalsmag.com/quotes-healing-inner-work/

Dizon, J. (n.d.). *Juansen Dizon quotes*. Goodreads. https://www.goodreads.com/author/quotes/16485155.Juansen_Dizon?page=2

Ego vs. inner child: What's the difference? (n.d.). *Inner Magic Academy*. https://www.innermagicacademy.com/blog/ego-inner-child-difference

Elizabeth, D. (2022, December 19). *44 affirmations for your inner child: Nurture and heal childhood traumas.* Wildsimplejoy.com. https://wildsimplejoy.com/affirmations-for-your-inner-child-healing/

Emotional wellness toolkit. (2017). National Institutes of Health (NIH). https://www.nih.gov/health-information/emotional-wellness-toolkit

Fierman, C. (2020, March 11). The story of Kake: A tale of healing our inner child. *Evoke Therapy Programs.* https://evoketherapy.com/resources/blog/claire-mattison/the-story-of-kake-a-tale-of-healing-our-inner-child/

Gatt, Dr. R. (2024, March 24). Identifying your trauma. *Woven Together Trauma Therapy.* https://woventraumatherapy.com/blog/identify-your-trauma

Gibson, L. (n.d.). *Lindsay C. Gibson quotes.* Goodreads. https://www.goodreads.com/quotes/9683620-children-who-try-to-be-good-enough-to-win-their

Gillespie, C. (2020, October 27). *What is generational trauma?* Health. https://www.health.com/condition/ptsd/generational-trauma

Haupt, A. (2023, April 6). *What to know about inner child work.* Time. https://time.com/6268636/inner-child-work-healing/

Hilary Brenner, G. (2017, November 18). Six elements of self-care in adults with childhood trauma. *Psychology Today.* https://www.psychologytoday.com/ca/blog/experimentations/201711/six-elements-self-care-in-adults-childhood-trauma

The history of CBT. (2023). Beck Institute Cares. https://cares.beckinstitute.org/about-cbt/history-of-cbt/

Jones, R. (2020, October 5). 25 positive affirmations to heal childhood trauma. *A Solution B, LLC.* https://www.asolutionb.com/chat-trap-blog/positive-affirmations-to-heal-childhood-trauma

Kaimal, G. (2020, June 3). *How art can heal.* American Scientist. https://www.americanscientist.org/article/how-art-can-heal

Lee, M., Lee, J., Park, B.-J., & Miyazaki, Y. (2015). Interaction with indoor plants may reduce psychological and physiological stress by suppressing autonomic nervous system activity in young adults: a randomized crossover study. *Journal of Physiological Anthropology, 34*(1). https://doi.org/10.1186/s40101-015-0060-8

Leonard, K., & Watts, R. (2022). *The ultimate guide to S.M.A.R.T. goals.* Forbes Advisor; Forbes. https://www.forbes.com/advisor/business/smart-goals/

Livia. (2022, January 25). *22 ways to connect with your inner child.* Madewithlemons.co. https://madewithlemons.co/connect-with-your-inner-child/

Mencius. (n.d.). *Mencius quotes.* Goodreads. https://www.goodreads.com/

quotes/1197940-great-is-the-man-who-has-not-lost-his-childlike

Merrick, M. T., Ford, D. C., Ports, K. A., Guinn, A. S., Chen, J., Klevens, J., Metzler, M., Jones, C. M., Simon, T. R., Daniel, V. M., Ottley, P., & Mercy, J. A. (2019). Vital signs: Estimated proportion of adult health problems attributable to adverse childhood experiences and implications for prevention — 25 states, 2015–2017. *MMWR. Morbidity and Mortality Weekly Report*, *68*(44), 999–1005. https://doi.org/10.15585/mmwr.mm6844e1

Mitts, C. (2019, September 3). *12 very common examples of trauma*. Ipseity Counseling in Denver. https://ipseitycounselingclinic.com/2019/09/03/examples-of-trauma/

Morrow, M. (2022, March 7). The history of cognitive behavioral therapy (CBT). *Klearminds*. https://www.klearminds.com/blog/history-cognitive-behavioural-therapy-cbt/

Nachmanovitch, S. (n.d.). *Stephen Nachmanovitch quotes*. Goodreads. https://www.goodreads.com/quotes/598226-the-most-potent-muse-of-all-is-our-own-inner

Navigating the holidays as an adult survivor of childhood abuse. (2021, November 24). EndCAN. https://endcan.org/2021/11/24/navigating-the-holidays-as-an-adult-survivor-of-childhood-abuse/

Pal, P., Hauck, C., Goldstein, E., Bobinet, K., & Bradley, C. (2018, December 13). *5 simple mindfulness practices for daily life*. Mindful. https://www.mindful.org/take-a-mindful-moment-5-simple-practices-for-daily-life/

Parashar, Dr. D. (2021, December 15). My experiences with inner child healing. *Dr Divya Parashar*. https://www.divyaparashar.com/blog/my-experiences-with-inner-child-healing

Riopel, L. (2019, June 14). *The importance, benefits, and value of goal setting*. Positive Psychology. https://positivepsychology.com/benefits-goal-setting/

Sauber Millacci, T. (2023, November 23). *7 trauma response types & how to recognize them*. PositivePsychology.com. https://positivepsychology.com/trauma-response/#4-typical-

Stanton, R. (2021, December 13). *7 myths about trauma*. Counseling in Boston LLC. https://counselinginboston.com/7-myths-about-trauma/

Towle, B. (2023, April 11). *I'm not enough (A personal story of limiting beliefs)*. Brendon Towle Coaching. https://brendontowlecoaching.com/2023/04/11/im-not-enough-a-personal-story-of-limiting-beliefs/

Using behavioral experiments to test your beliefs. (2020, November 14). Psychology Tools. https://www.psychologytools.com/self-help/behavioral-experi

ments/

Ward, E. (n.d.). *Big kid quotes*. Emma Ward - Business Confidence Coaching. https://www.emma-ward.com/big-kid-quotes

Weinberger, M. I., Mateo, C., & Sirey, J. A. (2009). Perceived barriers to mental health care and goal setting among depressed, community-dwelling older adults. *Patient Preference and Adherence, 3*, 145-149.

What is cognitive behavioral therapy? (2017). *American Psychological Association*. https://www.apa.org/ptsd-guideline/patients-and-families/cognitive-behavioral

Wu, R., Liu, L.-L., Zhu, H., Su, W.-J., Cao, Z.-Y., Zhong, S.-Y., Liu, X.-H., & Jiang, C.-L. (2019). Brief mindfulness meditation improves emotion processing. *Frontiers in Neuroscience, 13*. https://doi.org/10.3389/fnins.2019.01074

Image References

Images on the following pages were created with the assistance of Midjourney: 15, 38, 66, 94, 143, 175, 196